SOVIET
SCIENTIST
IN
RED CHINA

Mikhail A. Klochko

Translated by
ANDREW MacANDREW

FREDERICK A. PRAEGER, *Publisher*

New York

BOOKS THAT MATTER

Published in the United States of America in 1964
by Frederick A. Praeger, Inc., Publisher
111 Fourth Ave., New York 3, N.Y.

Library of Congress Catalog Card Number: 64-16681

Printed in the United States of America

Contents

Foreword

In August, 1961, I succeeded at last in fulfilling a wish I had had for a long time—to leave the Soviet Union and come to live in a democratic land. Now I live in Canada, and I can read any books, any newspapers, any journals that I want, no matter what part of the world they come from. I can talk without fear on any conceivable subject, with anyone I choose, and I can write down my thoughts.

When I arrived in Canada, one of the very first things I had done was to acquire all available material about the Communist bloc. What I found in the books and periodicals about Red China led me to the conclusion that a record of what I had seen and done in that country during my sojourns there in 1958 and 1960 might be of some interest to Western readers. As a Soviet scientist working in Peking, Kunming, and elsewhere, I had had the opportunity to observe certain aspects of Chinese life from a somewhat different angle from that presented by those authors who had spent a few weeks, or at best a few months, in China, or those who had left the country ten years ago, or those who had never been there at all. My travels in China were not limited to the standard tourist itineraries nor my contacts to interpreters and planted observers, such as are reserved for visitors from capitalist and even from other Communist countries. For I had occasion to talk to scores, even hundreds, of Chinese scientists, engineers, and administrators, ranging from those who were just out of college to well-established professors with decades of teaching experience.

These considerations persuaded me to write this book. I have not attempted to explain every aspect of life in China today: I have simply written down what I saw and heard and what I thought of it. In my position, I was obviously chiefly concerned with two aspects of modern China—the life and work of scientists there, and Sino-Soviet relations—but it goes without saying that there are many other matters that I both observed and wrote about.

I was born in the Ukraine, where I first attended a four-year municipal school, to which I was sent because the yearly tuition was only ten rubles instead of the sixty rubles charged at a complete secondary school. Later, I continued my secondary education in evening courses for adults.

Although the Bolsheviks had seized power in Petrograd in 1917, they did not control the Ukraine until almost three years later. In 1920, when the regime gained control, I enlisted in the Red Army as a volunteer. A year later, I began my higher education, and, when it was completed, I remained at the technical college to do scientific work. At the same time, I studied English, French, and German (using teach-yourself books), in order to read the indispensable literature for my field, chemistry, written in those languages.

For thirty-six years, from 1925 to 1961, I did research in chemistry; during the earlier years, I also taught—in Kiev and Moscow.

I was also sent on several special scientific missions abroad: to England and France (1934–35), to Austria (1956), to India (1959), and to China (1958 and 1960). I took advantage of my visits abroad to practice my English, French, and German, and I also tried to keep informed about the organization of research in physics and chemistry in those various countries.

Beginning in 1930, I worked in the Laboratory of General Chemistry, under the Soviet Academy of Sciences in Leningrad, which was headed by the well-known Russian scientist, Academician Nikolai Semyonovich Kurnakov. His interests extended to various areas of theoretical and inorganic chemistry, and he tried to develop a similar breadth of view in his pupils and collaborators. Thanks to him, I did not confine myself to any one special field, but worked in such varied areas as electrochemistry, the chemistry of natural salt lakes, theory of solutions, alloys, and other chemical systems, etc.

In 1934, the Academy of Sciences was moved to Moscow. There, the Laboratory of General Chemistry (where I worked) and the Institutes of Platinum and Physicochemical Analysis were organized into a single Institute of General and Inorganic Chemistry. Academician Kurnakov remained in charge of that Institute until his death in March, 1941. There, I received my diploma as a Candidate of Sciences in 1936; later, in December, 1940, I defended my doctoral dissertation in chemistry, and the doctorate was conferred on me.

In 1946, I was granted the title of Professor of Physical Chemistry, and, in 1948, I received the Stalin Prize for my work. I was given the Order of Merit and the Order of the Red Banner of Labor for my scientific achievements.

At the Institute of General and Inorganic Chemistry, I was in charge of the laboratory doing research on solutions, for I had given up teaching in 1941, and concentrated solely on research—

as far as that is possible in the Soviet Union, where a scientist, especially when he is also a Party member, must devote a considerable part of his time to so-called civic duties and Party assignments. Of the twenty scientists employed in my laboratory, about half of them worked under my direct supervision, while the rest worked independently and had their own assistants. I also had to give some of my time to editorial work for various scientific journals.

Although I occupied a relatively high position in the Soviet scientific hierarchy, I found the working conditions painful, and, in 1961, I took advantage of an opportunity to make a long-cherished dream come true—to move to a free country. On August 6 of that year, with my passport in my hand and my notebooks in my inside pocket against my heart, I faced the frightening eyes of a Soviet security police officer at the Moscow airport. I was on my way to an international conference of chemists to be held in Montreal. Shifting his eyes back and forth from me to my passport, the policeman finally stamped the document and handed it back to me. I sighed with relief and congratulated myself on having passed the first hurdle, yet I was still haunted by the vision of what would have happened if the officer had decided to search me and had discovered my notebooks, which so disapprovingly referred to the policy of the Soviet government toward China.

Before I had walked three steps, I heard his voice call after me, "Hey, Comrade Klochko, come back here a minute!"

Here it is, I thought, it's all up.

"Why is there no signature on your passport, Comrade Klochko?"

It turned out that on my passport, with which I had gone all the way to China and back in 1960, my signature was missing.

Somehow, no one had ever noticed it before. I hurriedly took a pen and scrawled my name.

After that, I safely passed the medical authorities and customs. Already feeling almost a free man, I walked through the airport terminal toward the gate leading to the plane. Since the gate was not yet open, I picked up an airline pamphlet and was desultorily turning its pages when I heard someone call my name. I looked up to see the customs official who had inspected my bags. Once again, with a piercing sharpness, the feeling of deadly danger came over me. But the man was smiling politely: He simply wanted to give me my luggage receipt, which I had left with the customs officials. The air rushed back into my lungs once again.

It was only one hour later, when the plane finally took off, that I said to myself, "In one hundred minutes, I shall be beyond Soviet territory."

Nine days later, on August 15, 1961, I took the most important step of my life: I asked the Canadian authorities for political asylum. My request was granted.

After the Communist victory in continental China, the Soviet Union began to aid the new Chinese Communist state in development and industrialization. By 1956, there were already a considerable number of Soviet scientists and technicians in China. In 1958, I was sent too, for six months, at the request of the Chinese Academy of Sciences, but my stay was extended to seven and a half months. My second sojourn there was interrupted by the dramatic events of the summer of 1960, so I stayed only five months. But during those two trips, I talked with hundreds of my Chinese colleagues; Chinese friends kept in contact with me even after I returned to the Soviet Union; and conversations with other Soviet specialists who had been to China also contributed to my understanding of the events of the time. I received my last information about the situation within China in the spring of 1961.

While in China, I had not been content simply to observe the life around me—I read all the available literature about the country published in China in Russian or English. I read books on Chinese history, philosophy, and literature (mostly in English, since only very few were in Russian), the most important Party and government documents, the writings and speeches of Mao Tse-tung, Chou En-lai, Liu Shao-chi, and other prominent officials. I also kept a diary, in which I noted down everything connected with my work, the dates and subjects of the lectures I gave, the conferences I attended, and the talks I had when visiting various educational and industrial establishments in different cities. I used all this material in the oral and written accounts I gave of my Chinese experiences when I returned to Moscow. Besides that official diary, I jotted down impressions of meetings and conversations; I brought these notes with me to Canada and have used them in working on this book.

I have not selected or sifted the facts to make them fit the pattern of any possible preconceived ideas I or my readers may have. If correct conclusions are to be drawn and the proper steps decided on in any field, one must be acquainted with all the facts, pleasant or unpleasant. But I have tried not to overburden the book with too detailed a description of my scientific work in China, for I fear this would be of little interest to my readers.

In writing this book, I have lived over again all the things I saw and heard in China during my two visits there. I have seen in my mind's eye China's beautiful natural landscapes and the wonderfully kind people whom I met there. The broad, straight, tree-lined avenues of Changchun, the temples, palaces and walls of Peking, the driveway lined with ancient trees where I drove each day from my hotel to the Research Institute—I have seen them all unroll before me in my remembrances of that beautiful land. I know I shall never forget the magnificent vistas leading to Hangchow, or the green, wooded hills of Yünnan with the beautiful Buddhist monasteries half hidden amidst the foliage. But engraved deepest in my memory are the human faces—gay and sad, intelligent and subtle, or visages turned dull and dim by hardship and backbreaking toil—the faces of the Chinese I met in laboratories, factories, hotels, parks, stores, and on the streets. For China is for me no longer an exotic land of ancient culture, consummate customs, and a refined cuisine. It is an immense nation inhabited by hundreds of millions of famished people, whose primary preoccupation is simply to stay alive, who are unable to profit from China's ancient heritage, and who must instead serve as the raw material over which one man strives to prove his power.

If there are any Chinese among my future readers, I would like to apologize to them for certain passages that will displease them. I wish to emphasize here that the criticisms I voice are not against any particular traits of the Chinese people, whom I love and respect, but of certain conditions of the country, both past and present. Those conditions are transitory and, as they disappear, the unfavorable phenomena accompanying them will also vanish. Then the great qualities of the Chinese people—their industry, their wisdom, their peacefulness, their love of beauty—will shine brighter than ever.

M. A. K.

Canada
May, 1964

PART ONE

China, 1958

CHAPTER ONE

A Scientific Assignment

In the U.S.S.R., I had no access to foreign literature on China, so I had no very precise idea of the latest developments there or of the modern Chinese way of life when, in the fall of 1956, I was summoned to the personnel section of the Soviet Academy of Sciences and asked whether I would like to go to China for two years to organize research work there. The offer was, of course, interesting and most tempting, but two years seemed much too long to be away from Moscow. After years of effort, I had just managed to organize a small, efficient group in my laboratory, and working with these colleagues was a real pleasure. If I was gone long, the group would disintegrate, my people and equipment would be grabbed by other labs, and there would be nothing to come back to. So I refused, despite the insistence of a lady in the personnel section of the Academy who tried to use a sort of stick-and-carrot method on me, and I quite firmly insisted that I would not leave Moscow for more than six months. The aforesaid lady then offered the same China project to two of my colleagues, and when they also refused to be absent from Moscow for two full years, she summoned Dr. Nina Luzhnaya, who didn't even have a lab of her own at the time, and it was agreed that Luzhnaya would go to China for six months.

Luzhnaya left early in 1957 and returned five months later. From the report she made on her return to our Institute of Chemistry in Moscow, we learned that she had worked in Peking at the Research Institute of Chemistry, under the Chinese Academy of Sciences, and that she had also been to other cities, including Changchun and Shanghai. She conveyed the impression that there were very few trained chemists in China, and that her going there had been not only a great boon for Chinese science but a godsend for the entire country. The group of lady scientists who for all practical purposes ran our Institute (among whom Luzhnaya played an important part) tried to strengthen this version of the story even further.

I must explain here that in any establishment under the Soviet Academy of Sciences, there is, alongside the appointed officers—the director, his assistants, and the leading scientists—an unofficial group that actually controls everything that goes on. Usually, these people are old but not very able scientists, mostly (but not always) Party members, who attempt to compensate for their professional limitations by making pompous pronouncements and by persecuting all the honest and more gifted scientists who refuse to dance to their tune—or who simply refuse to work for them. These people determine who gets the awards and who gets promoted; they also assign apartments, an important item in view of the severe housing shortage in the Soviet Union. Sometimes, members of this group belong to the institute's board of directors, but they are mostly from each institute's bureau of the Party organization, which consists of seven to eleven members elected by the Party rank and file. The Party bureaus decide all internal matters at the institutes, and in every Soviet establishment, the secretary of the Party bureau is an extremely powerful person with whom the directors must strive to find a means of peaceful coexistence.

Since most of the scientists in our Institute were women, it naturally followed that the really powerful members of this "leading group" were also women, although there were a few men who functioned as their toadies. The group came to be referred to as the "Old Wives' Committee" (*Babkom*). The Old Wives' Committee considerably affected my work at the Institute and also the evaluation of my work in China. Like many other "unsympathetic" and "rebellious" members of the Institute, I was subject to all sorts of persecution from these women, while their toadies were constantly praised and rewarded.

One day in August, 1957, I was working in my vegetable garden in Domodedovo, a development about thirty miles from Moscow where members of the Institute had been issued small plots of land on which they could build country cottages. Luzhnaya's plot was not far from mine, and I saw her approaching, accompanied by another lady. Luzhnaya was at that time deputy director of the Institute, and her companion, Medvedeva, was secretary of the Party bureau.

When I asked them what could be the reason for my being honored with a holiday visit from two such illustrious ladies at my humble abode, they told me they wanted to talk to me about my departure for China. I was stupefied.

"I remember you said last year you'd be willing to go for six months," Luzhnaya said calmly. "Well, a chemist is needed in your field to go there for just that length of time."

"Yes," Medvedeva confirmed, "you'd be the most suitable person for the assignment."

After politely admiring my vegetable patch, the two august ladies departed in stately procession.

5

When my vacation was over in September, I began to prepare for my trip.

In 1956, the Government of the People's Republic of China had started to think about the development of the country's science in terms of a long-range plan. After the matter had been debated at various Party and government levels, a Planning Committee for Scientific Development was entrusted with drafting a twelve-year plan. For several months, a score of Chinese scientists and their Soviet counterparts worked on this plan, which was first approved by the Chinese Communist Party and then sent to the Soviet Union in the fall of 1957. In the Soviet Union, it was examined by various groups of Soviet specialists and later discussed at joint meetings with Chinese scientists (120 of them). Groups of specialists—in organic chemistry, inorganic chemistry, applied chemistry, etc.—went over each relevant problem in the plan.

The basic objective of this twelve-year plan was for China to catch up to the level of world science in all the main theoretical and, above all, practical areas within twelve years, i.e., by the end of 1967. The Soviet scientists were expected not only to evaluate the objectives the Chinese had chosen in this plan, but also to designate those problems that could be coped with jointly by the scientific forces of the two countries. Indeed, it was decided that almost 100 out of the 580 problems would thus be handled.

Of course, in 1957, during the period when "fraternal relations" between China and the U.S.S.R. were at their closest—as we were assured by the official information sources—there was nothing more natural for the People's Republic than to turn for help to the "beacon light of world Communism," the "source of Marxist-Leninist wisdom"—that is, to the Soviet Union. But, as it turned out later, 95 per cent of all that planning was a waste of time, since the progress of Chinese science started to slow down in 1957 and came to a complete standstill in 1959. (It was only two years later, toward the middle of 1961, that a slight movement became detectable once again.)

Almost all the problems specified in the Chinese plan were problems in applied science, although theoretical aspects were mentioned now and then. The Soviet scientists based their evaluation of these matters on their own experience, being, as they were, unfamiliar with the state of science in China and with its limitations. For instance, various members of our Chemistry Institute, myself included, were invited to help the Chinese with various problems of inorganic chemistry. But the work was not properly organized: We were never given an opportunity to acquaint ourselves with the level of Chinese chemical research; in fact, we never learned what the actual planned schedule was. In the Karpov Institute of Chemistry in Moscow, where the work was done, three committees would hold simultaneous meetings in one medium-sized room; a section of the plan would be read out and our opinion asked about whether this or that should be done by the Chinese alone or by combined Sino-Russian efforts. But, as might have been foreseen, the main element was lacking: No single living person stood behind any of these plans or any one of the scientific issues they covered; no one person was in a position to organize a group of even two or three scientists who would give their all to solving a particular problem, or who would at least train younger technicians to handle the task. There was no enthusiasm and no organization—in short, the whole enterprise was lifeless.

Several years have elapsed since this planning work was done in Moscow. I believe that of the almost six hundred scientific and technological projects foreseen in the twelve-year plan, only a few isolated units are still going concerns, and even those have only barely managed to survive.

There were several delays over my trip, and I made daily visits to the Foreign Section of the Academy of Sciences, which is staffed, incidentally, by a strange mixture of people—some from the Foreign Affairs Ministry, some from the Ministry of Internal Affairs (the MVD, formerly known as the NKVD), and some who had mistakenly chosen a scientific career, only to realize that they were totally unprepared and unfit for it. Finally, the date of my departure was set for January 8, 1958, and a place reserved for me on the plane leaving late that night for Peking from Vnukovo airport.

No one could have called it a pleasant trip. Bad weather forced the pilot to make unscheduled stops along the way, and each airport seemed colder and less pleasant than the last. Among the passengers—most of them Chinese, although the young man seated next to me looked less Chinese than Russian, yet spoke both languages with equal fluency—the Russians complained loudly and at length about the food, the service, and the complete inadequacy of the airline's managerial competence. But eventually, the clouds parted, the Great Wall lay below us like a delicate gray snake streaked across the crests of the hills, and soon we were nearing Peking.

I wondered who would meet me in Peking. The Foreign Section of the Academy had wired them of my impending arrival, but still, there was no one there who knew me or whom I knew. All I had been told was that I was going to work in Peking's Research Institute of Chemistry, and that the name of its director was Liu Ta-kang.

When we landed in Peking, I saw out of the window several groups of people waiting to meet us.

"There's Liu Ta-kang," my neighbor said, pointing in the general direction of a cluster of people standing on the snowy field. As we emerged from the plane, the group came toward me and greeted me effusively. There was Liu Ta-kang himself, his deputy, Hua Shao-chun; the man assigned to be my interpreter, Li Fu-teh; a member of the Institute, Madame Su Sao-bai; the secretary of the Institute, Liu Ssu-kuang; and finally, a small woman who was introduced as a member of the Academy of Sciences and a poetess. They led me to their open car, and Professor Liu installed himself next to me. To my great joy, it turned out that he spoke English. He had a friendly face and ready smile, but I thought there was something rather sad about the expression in his eyes.

We reached the city, and our car drove past endless rows of one-story shops topped by puzzling Chinese signs; advertisements on the windows and doors revealed their business to me. As we passed shops, slums, temples, or palaces, Professor Liu would tell me what the latter were and what their history had been.

We went over two or three railroad crossings, drove along a high wall, then turned right, and followed a magnificent driveway running between century-old trees, their branches swaying slowly in the evening twilight. Suddenly, the car came to a stop in front of a large, seven-story building: We had arrived at the famous Hotel Druzhba, the Friendship Hotel, where I was destined to spend, with the exception of a few intervals, more than seven months. With great relief, I quickly settled into my new home.

CHAPTER TWO

Science and Scientists in Peking

When I had been in Peking for a full day, Professor Liu and my interpreter, Li Fu-teh, picked me up at the hotel and took me to the Institute of Chemistry, where I was to work. We drove back along the tree-lined avenue, past the road to the Summer Palace, arriving at last in a district of low, gray houses with the taller buildings of the institutes standing out among them. This was the new northwestern suburb of Peking, called Chung Kuang-tsung, a growing academic suburb and yet unfinished *cité universitaire*.

The car stopped before a handsome, five-story house stuccoed with pale gray plaster. The central structure had large windows; two lower wings contained a library and an auditorium. Inside, long corridors branched off on either side of a wide staircase; they were illuminated by the light coming through glass doors that led to rooms on either side, and by windows at the end of each hall. Off the landings of the main staircase were the rooms used as offices or lecture halls. Most of the remaining space was taken up with laboratories—all of them large, well-lit, neatly arranged, and quite well equipped. Of the five stories of the main building, the Institute of Chemistry then occupied the three lower ones; the other two belonged to the Institute of Physics.

In the courtyard, there was another building, housing an X-ray lab and glass-blowing and machine shops—the laboratory as well equipped as ours in Moscow. As for the library, it had a light, spacious reading room, with many foreign books and periodicals (among them, the *Encyclopaedia Britannica*) that were absent from the library of our Institute in Moscow.

All the rooms, I was soon to learn, were kept in exemplary order and cleanliness. A tall, kindly-looking, middle-aged Chinese, who every morning would fill our thermoses with hot water for tea, spent the rest of the day polishing the floors and cleaning the rooms. That quiet, efficient man performed all by himself the work of the eight noisy women in ragged overalls who worked at the Institute in Moscow—which, despite all their rushing about, was far from being a model of neatness or cleanliness.

By the main entrance to the Institute, on a landing of the central staircase, I found, on that morning of my first visit, a blackboard with a carefully drawn inscription in red chalk, saying in Russian: "Welcome to our dear teacher, Professor M. A. Klochko." This gave me an unpleasant feeling, somehow. The phrase seemed obsequious.

I was taken into a large room where about twenty leading members of the Institute and its administrative staff had gathered to meet me. In front of each person, there was a little enamel cup with a lid, into which boiling water from the thermoses was constantly poured for new cups of tea.

When I first entered, Professor Liu at once delivered a little welcoming address in Chinese, which my interpreter simultaneously translated for my benefit. I was then introduced to the heads of the various departments, and it was agreed that I would first acquaint myself with the Institute, after which we would draw up a working schedule. So I spent the next three days going around the labs talking to the technical staff, going back again and again to the labs where scientists were working in my field, in order to study the work done in inorganic and physical chemistry in greater detail.

In the Institute, I was assigned for an office a room that was totally bare of laboratory apparatus. In the Soviet Union, I had never had even the smallest office at my personal disposal where I could work in peace, do the necessary reading, and prepare my experimental work. It was only now, after thirty-three years of scientific work, eighteen years after receiving my doctorate, ten years after becoming a professor and a laureate of the Stalin Prize, that I at last had my own little corner . . . and not in the Soviet Union, where I had worked all my life, but in remote China.

The Chemistry Institute was not officially subdivided into departments, but there were four groups that roughly corresponded to such a division, in inorganic, analytic, organic, and high-polymer chemistry. There were also labs for physical chemistry and the physicochemical study of polymeric compounds. Those in charge of labs or groups did not have official titles, such as Professor or Instructor, nor did they have academic degrees like the M.A. or Ph.D., which do not exist in China. But it did not take me long to realize that most of them had qualifications in no way lower than those of Soviet professors teaching at provincial colleges, and that at least five or six of the leading Institute members were easily the equal of a man holding a doctorate in science from Moscow University. All of them had been highly trained either in the United States or some other Western country, and, like most Chinese scientists, they spoke of American and West European scientists with the greatest respect. It was a source of pride for one of them that he had been the pupil of a particularly well-known Western scientist. In any event, we Soviet specialists used the title "Professor" as a courtesy in correspondence and in conversation with leading Chinese scientists.

Professor Liu Ta-kang was in charge of a group of inorganic chemists studying natural salts, but along with his experimental work, he performed his duties as director of the Institute. His predecessor in that job had also been a deputy minister of education, who was dismissed for his "right-wing deviationism" and, in 1957, sent into the country "among the masses" to do his penance and reconsider his views. Liu, a mild and intelligent man, was much easier for the authorities to deal with; in 1959, he was even accepted into the Party. Now in his late fifties, Liu had once studied in the United States and had done research on the optics of solutions there. Back in China, he had worked on various problems in applied chemistry, including a study of natural brines. During the Japanese invasion, he had fled to unoccupied territory in southwest China and worked there with other patriotic scientists.

Most of the senior members of the Institute combined their work there with teaching at Peking University or other institutions. Professor Huan Tzu-chin was the head of research in physical chemistry and lectured on that subject at Peking University. He too had studied and done research in the United States. A large, thickset man of about sixty, with a large round head and intelligent eyes, Huan spoke fluent English and German, chain-smoked furiously, and was renowned as an expert on the history of science in China. He was full of creative zeal and scientific projects, but the conditions for research prevailing in China in 1957–60—and probably still existing to this day—prevented him from carrying out his plans effectively and, for that matter, from teaching chemistry the way he felt chemistry should be taught. Still, any Soviet specialist in that field would have been proud of his achievements. During the Japanese occupation, he had worked in unoccupied Kunming in southern China, where he displayed, besides his scientific gifts, great administrative talents. He left an excellent impression among the local scientists there, who, as I found out later when I went to Kunming in 1960, were proud to refer to themselves as his pupils. Professor Huan was a sort of directorial consultant at the Institute in Peking, but the actual laboratory work was done under the supervision of a kindly assistant professor, Po.

The section on organic chemistry, perhaps the largest in the Institute and engaged primarily in research on synthetic fuels, was run by Professor Min, a shy, reserved man, but very nice. One of the specialists there was T'ao K'un, who previously had spent two years studying in the Soviet Union and who spoke Russian. There was also a married couple in their early thirties, who were famous throughout the Institute for their affection for each other and because they spent all their free moments together. They reminded me of the time in the 1950's when the authorities in the Soviet Union waged a campaign against "excessive family spirit." The purpose of it—if one can really find a purpose behind such Party campaigns—was to prevent a wife from working under her husband's supervision, for fear that he might be led to favor her over others. But, in fact, the campaign degenerated into a persecution of husbands and wives working in the same establishment, whatever their respective positions. Meanwhile, the sweethearts of the mighty, who were receiving crumbs from the public spoils in exchange for their secret, private "cooperation," went unmolested. Apparently, however, that particular stupid campaign had not yet spread to China in 1958.

The section for research on polymeric compounds was headed by Professor Wang Pao-chen, another American-trained chemist, who had organized the work of the five men and two women who made up his staff with remarkable efficiency. Professor Wang himself, by the way, complained that suggestions made by his lab were rejected by the synthetic-fibers industry, which preferred to use foreign patents that were in no way superior to the methods he proposed. In that connection, I remembered a case from a few years before in the Soviet Union—I believe it was in the field of silico-organic compounds. The industry had rejected a method proposed by a Russian scientist and had used instead an American process for which, of course, a tidy sum had to be paid. It had turned out, however, that the Americans were using methods devised by that same Russian scientist (whose findings had been published), methods that had been rejected in his homeland.

There was yet another small lab in the Institute where work was done on the physical chemistry of high-polymeric compounds. Most of the time, only one man worked there, Professor Chien, who had devised an excellent instrument for measuring the properties of polymeric solutions and had received a national award for it in 1957.

After I had looked around the Institute and became acquainted with its activities, we set about deciding in what way I would be most useful, and Professor Liu and I drafted my work plan for the next six months. The result was a final proposal that was translated into Chinese and sent to the directors of the Chinese Academy of Sciences. From there, the plan came back in Russian and Chinese, three copies in each language, for me and for the Institute. The Academy had made practically no changes in it.

According to the plan, I was to give lectures, take charge of the research in my field done by members of the Institute, be available for consultation on any subject in which I was competent (the invitation to consult me was extended to other research establishments in Peking upon their request), visit other groups that required my assistance, etc. Besides the work in Peking, I was scheduled to go on lecture tours in Changchun, Mukden (Shenyang), Shanghai, Nanking, and some other cities, and to make myself available for consultation with research groups there.

Although the main subject of my lectures was to be that part of theoretical chemistry which is called physicochemical analysis and which deals with the properties of chemical systems—i.e., solutions, alloys, and other mixtures—my consultations were also supposed to cover various matters of inorganic chemistry and applied electrochemistry, in which I had had some experience. I had brought only brief outlines for these lectures with me, but Chou Su-fen, a young student who was to translate them as I went along, asked me to write them out so that she could prepare the translations in advance. So we proceeded as follows: I would write down a lecture in Russian, using my outline; Su-fen would prepare tables based on the diagrams I had drawn. (Each lecture was thirty or forty manuscript pages and had about the same number of diagrams.) She would read the Russian text, marking the passages she could not understand, and I would explain them to her. Only after many such discussions were my lectures ready to be delivered in public. We gave them in a small auditorium, designed for 100 people at most; besides the members of the Institute, teachers from Peking University and from other establishments attended. Counting a fifteen-minute intermission, our lectures usually lasted three hours, with an additional question period, when Su-fen again acted as interpreter.

During many years of working in often poorly ventilated laboratories, my throat had been damaged by the fumes of acids and by pernicious gases, and this had caused my voice to become hoarse. In my rather weak, scratchy voice, I would read my lectures a few sentences at a time, but Su-fen's translation of my works resounded clearly, as pure as a silver bell. It was always a matter of wonder to me how such a little creature as she, who was no taller than a child, could have such a powerful, resounding voice, strong enough even for large auditoriums, as I found out later when I lectured in other cities. Sometimes, to explain certain special terms, she wrote, with breathtaking speed, Chinese characters on the blackboard. Traced by her, they looked very neat and pretty.

Because Su-fen articulated very clearly, the sounds she made gradually became familiar to me, as, time and again, I compared them with their Russian equivalents. On a few rare occasions, I was even able to discern that her translation had not covered all the points I had made, and I would discreetly try to prompt her.

Between February and June, 1958, I gave twelve lectures in Peking, and the only difficulty that arose was due to the innumerable meetings and conferences that were held almost every day, sometimes consuming the entire working day of the Institute members. Often, even Su-fen had no time to prepare her translations and had to do them late at night, sacrificing hours of sleep. Beginning in May, we ran into further trouble with the lecture schedule. A fixed schedule prepared in advance was out of the question, since no one could possibly guess when the Party organization of the Institute or Academy would decide to call its scheduled or non-scheduled meetings, but it would always be during working hours, taking the members of the Institute away from their own work. As time passed, the number of such meetings increased. In January and February, they took up two full days a week, then three; by June and July, meetings were called almost every day, so that the Chinese scientists had no choice but to do their research at night. My lectures had to be postponed, often indefinitely, and gradually, members of the University ceased to attend altogether, for almost all of them were sent out to factories and to the country.

In fact, throughout my stay in China in 1958, as I sadly witnessed the constant reduction in the working time in the labs because of the ever increasing number of these meetings, I began to realize that they threatened the Institute with real disaster. In the Soviet Union, political meetings at least were not allowed during working hours, so that they less directly menaced our scientific work. But in China, it came to the point where it was almost impossible to find anyone at his job at the usual hours at his usual place of work.

Once, just after nine in the morning, Su-fen pulled a little pillow out of her desk drawer, a small footstool from under the table, and, carrying these two items, walked toward the door.

"Where are you off to, Su-fen?" I asked her.

"I have to go and listen to Comrade Tuh, the secretary of the Party organization of the Academy. He is reporting on his trip to the Soviet Union. Everyone working for the Academy must go and hear his report," she said.

Shortly after she left, I heard a voice coming over the loudspeakers that were installed in every corridor. I opened the door and saw that the entire passage was cluttered with people, some, like Su-fen, sitting on footstools, others on the floor. It must have been rather hard on them, for Comrade Tuh's voice poured out at them all day without letup, except during the sacred lunch hour, when he fell silent.

"That fellow dares call himself a Party secretary!" I thought to myself. "Some Party secretary, wasting the whole day of several thousand workers with his drivel!" I couldn't understand why he had not limited his report to one or even two hours and made it after work, or why he had not simply had the report printed and distributed.

But the epidemic of such reports and discussions spread, so that by August, 1958, whatever scientific work was still going on petered out completely throughout all of China. Research in the labs came to a stop, lectures at the Institute were discontinued, teaching at the higher-education institutions ceased for all practical purposes. It was only on occasional nights that people engaged in "scientific work" and then as a "present to the Party and to Comrade Mao" for some festive date such as July 1, the anniversary of the founding of the Chinese Communist Party. But how much can one accomplish in a few nights, when one has been exhausted during the day by endless sterile discussions and mutual denunciations? It goes without saying that those "presents" made no substantial scientific or practical contribution to Chinese science, being of a purely symbolic nature. They were a most shameless bluff. And bluff is typical of present-day China. When, for instance, a research team at some institute obtained a gram of platinum from their experimental residues, they triumphantly announced: "We are producing our own platinum!" But obtaining one gram of platinum from lab residues is a far cry from producing the metal from natural ore on an industrial basis.

My efforts to organize basic research proved vain, as the Institute drifted with the winds of Party directives, changing direction every few months. Later, the Institute ceased to make any headway at all and started to spin madly in one spot. All work came to a virtual standstill, and the members of the Institute spent their days regurgitating the wisdom of the five great sages—Marx, Engels, Lenin, Stalin, and Mao—and "exposing" each other at endless self-criticism meetings. I had made a close study of the basic research projects the Institute had been engaged in and had suggested new subjects for investigation, but during those short seven months, what programs there were, were changed without consulting me, and the subjects I had suggested were replaced by others. Research at the Institute disintegrated before my eyes, not simply out of disregard for my program but because of the systematic disorganization of all Chinese scientific research which the Party had undertaken. Apparently, there was a great deal of pressure put on the Institute from above to engage in research that, according to the ignorant Party leaders, was more directly connected with national requirements in industry and agriculture. (The topics for research that Luzhnaya had proposed in 1957 had met with the same fate.)

For my part, I did my best to carry out the work for which I was being paid. I arose at six-thirty each morning, as the loudspeakers in the Friendship Hotel blared Chinese military marches. I breakfasted in the hotel and left for my office at around eight o'clock where, as a rule, Su-fen was already waiting for me. The tall, kindly Chinese I had noticed on my first day soon came in to fill our thermoses with boiling water. A box of green tea, a teapot, and six china cups were next to the thermoses. During the ritual of tea, we went over the schedule for the day, then prepared my lectures, and went on my rounds of the labs, unless there was someone waiting to consult me.

At ten o'clock, the loudspeakers all over the Institute summoned everyone to the compulsory daily session of "physical culture," a series of exercises done to music. At noon, a bell rang, and all my colleagues went to the dining hall for lunch, while I left to spend the two-hour break at my hotel.

Once, having some materials to prepare, I returned to the Institute a half-hour earlier than usual. As I entered the building, it seemed completely deserted—there was not a living soul on the stairs or in the corridors. But when I opened the door of my office, I was greeted with the most remarkable and surprising scene:

Several Chinese girls who worked at the Institute had transformed the place into a dormitory for an afternoon siesta. They now rose, frightened and embarrassed by my intrusion, while Su-fen apologized profusely for taking advantage of my absence and allowing herself and some of her friends to catch up on their sleep. I apologized in my turn for having disturbed them, gathered up my papers, and went to work in the library.

I usually wound up my work at about six-thirty and returned to the hotel. At the Institute, dinner was served at seven sharp. This punctuality was strictly observed, and neither work nor political meetings was allowed to interfere with the sacrosanct event. Even Su-fen, such a model of industry and calm, would begin to display signs of impatience when the appointed hour approached. At first, I did not notice this attitude toward the meals and caused her to be late in the dining hall, but later I saw to it that she shouldn't be a moment late. Perhaps she believed in the ancient saying "The latercomer gets nothing but the bones," although, with meat being a rare treat, the phrase was not really applicable. I suppose the first arrivals had a better chance of buying some supplement to the main dish to which their card entitled them. In any case, the lectures I gave began at two-thirty and finished in good time for Su-fen's dinner, but if a consultation went on too long, we made it clear to the visitor that the mealtime was drawing near and that the consultation must end. As a rule, we fixed the office hours for out-of-town visitors early in the afternoon so that they would not possibly interfere with Su-fen's dinner.

The people who came to consult me usually came one or two at a time. Su-fen would pour tea for us all, and, over tea, the visitors explained what their problems or questions were. Often, I could answer them immediately, but occasionally, I would ask them to return later, if their query required me to do some reading on the subject first.

Once, two men and a woman from Peking University came to see me who wanted to know whom they could invite from the Soviet Union to organize research in inorganic synthesis. I told them that none of the four or five famous Soviet specialists in that field whom I knew of—all of them Academicians or corresponding members of the Academy—would be sent to China. As for other possibilities, I felt certain they could find people in China who were just as well qualified. I advised them to organize the classes and research themselves, using their own personnel; that would, in itself, be a useful and educative experience. They argued for a long time and left, as far as I could gather, quite dissatisfied.

Later, it transpired that they had not taken my advice and had asked for a Soviet specialist without specifying anyone in particular. This was rather typical: The Chinese were always asking for "a chemist," "a physicist" or whatever, without naming any one person, not realizing that the Soviet government was reluctant to send a top man to China unless he had been asked for specifically. China was in somewhat the same situation as the Ukrainian bride in the story: She had nothing to offer but money, and "a rich suitor wouldn't want her, while a poor suitor wouldn't dare." Actually, experts poor in knowledge usually did "dare" to go to China, and many Soviet specialists imagined there was little difference between the state of science in China and in some country in central Africa.

One day, during the summer, a man came to see me from Szechwan, where salt has long been obtained from underground deposits. The use of that salt for food has caused illness and even death, and an investigation revealed that the table salt obtained there contained poisonous barium salts. My young visitor explained that the people of Szechwan, now in the middle of their "Great Leap Forward," and inspired by Party directives and the wise instructions of Comrade Mao Tse-tung, wished to develop the extraction processes at these natural deposits so as to exploit the presence of other compounds of elements in them—potassium, magnesium, strontium, boron, iodine, etc. He showed me two alternative plans for the complete processing of the deposits and asked which of the two I thought would be more suitable, or whether there was a third, even better, way. I examined the diagrams; they were not difficult to understand, for most of the symbols used were international ones, while the few odd Chinese characters stood for phrases familiar to any chemist, such as "preheating," "dissolving," "evaporating." With Su-fen's assistance, I could easily grasp their meaning.

I told my visitor that the plans seemed well conceived, but that I could not pass judgment on them without a complete chemical analysis of the deposits and full economic data on the cost of raw materials, labor, the price of the finished products, etc. Without that information, I explained, neither I nor any other scientist could possibly give him a dependable evaluation of his scheme. The young Chinese looked very disappointed.

"But I came especially to get expert assistance," he said.

I tried to cheer him up, assuring him that I felt he was on the right track, and recommending some special reading in the field—most of the books being available in the Institute library. He replied that he had come for only three days and did not have time to work in the library. I told him further that Professor I. P. Lepeshkov, who was a Soviet expert on natural salts, was expected in Peking and perhaps would have more to say about the problem than I. But to no avail. My young visitor, like many other young Chinese scientists and technicians I met, expected me, like every Soviet specialist, to be a sort of magician, capable of giving them the one correct answer to all sorts of complex problems in pure and applied science in a few minutes.

Here I would like to relate one very curious incident that occurred in connection with my duties as a consultant. One day, Su-fen informed me that a young man wished to speak to me about something or other, but she did not tell me who he was or where he came from. At the appointed time, a rather well-dressed young man came to my office and asked me questions about various alloys. There was something familiar about his face but I could not remember where I had seen him before. After our official consultation was over, we had a friendly chat. His Russian was excellent, and I thought his voice was familiar too.

"How do you feel here in Peking?" he inquired. "How do you like the climate?"

"As you can see," I said, pointing to the teapot, "I have become completely naturalized and completely Chinese: I drink tea all day during my office hours."

"That's the right thing to do, here in the dry Peking climate." And then, I suddenly remembered. Why, he had sat next to me in the plane coming to Peking! It turned out that he worked in the Institute of Physics.

"We have the best labs and workshops in China," he said. "But unfortunately," he added, "we spend more time at meetings and conferences than at our jobs."

I liked hearing this correct and daring evaluation of the state of affairs coming from a young Chinese scientist. He took leave of me, promising to come and see me again, and to show me around the Physics Institute. In fact, he did come again, but he never invited me to the physics labs in return. I understood that they were working on nuclear physics there, and a visit by a Soviet scientist was not welcome at the time.

When he had left, I told Su-fen, "I sat next to that young man on the plane from Moscow to Peking. I suppose he is some graduate student, isn't he?"

Actually, the young man's visit had caused a considerable to-do, for he was none other than the son of Liu Shao-chi, then Chairman of the Standing Committee of the National People's Congress, a man second to none but Mao in China. (In April, 1959, he replaced Mao as Chairman of the People's Republic of China, and his former position was taken over by Marshal Chu Teh.)

All sorts of rumors circulated about Liu Shao-chi. Many considered him to be the leader of the "pro-Russian clique," and, incidentally, he looked very Russian to me, much more so than an acquaintance of mine who is of purely Russian stock. Everyone wondered at the dizzying speed of his political rise, for although he was supposed to be one of the "Party theoreticians," he had never said anything strikingly original. It is doubtful in any case whether one has a chance to say anything original so long as Mao is alive, without jeopardizing, if not one's life, at least one's career. And there is no doubt that an important part in Liu's career was his closeness to Mao. In short, the quip a Russian expert in China made about Chinese politicians is applicable to Liu Shao-chi: "A Chinese is like a thermos: It is impossible to tell from the outside whether the contents are hot or cold."

Liu Shao-chi's son had lived in the Soviet Union for most of his childhood, studied there at school and at the university, and now worked as a physicist in Peking.

During my early days at the Institute, I had some difficulty understanding how its hierarchy was organized and how it was actually administered. At that time, its director, Liu Ta-kang, was not a Party member. He was a "non-Party scientist," as such persons are called in the Soviet Union. His all-powerful deputy, however, Hua Shao-chun, was a Party member all right, and a veteran of the civil war, a man without any higher education—without any education at all, for all I know. There was also the scientific secretary of the Institute, Liu Ssu-kuang, a specialist in organic chemistry who was quite good at research and who was later transferred to an administrative post at the Academy.

Research programs, which were discussed at innumerable meetings, were determined by the government's scientific advisory councils, and their decisions were communicated to the Institute through the Academy. (This administrative work was hopelessly slowed down by the typing problem: The secretariat of the Institute had one Chinese typewriter at its disposal, an ancient model with 1,200 characters. Typing took about ten times longer than on any Russian typewriter. The Institute had no learned council of leading scientists, no curriculum committee, no cooperative council that could discuss the programs, study reports, and evaluate the findings and opinions of the individual research workers, as was done in our Moscow Institute. From time to time, however, conferences were called to which other experts in Peking and from out of town were invited. The Academy of Sciences also arranged conferences at which the programs of various institutes working in the same field were examined and compared.

I attended one such conference. It was devoted to the matter of processing rare elements and was held at the Academy between May 2 and May 5, 1958. On that occasion, I had another interpreter besides Su-fen, and the two of them took turns whispering the Russian translation of the proceedings into my ear. The impression I got was that every one of the institutes and groups represented there claimed to be fully qualified to process all sixty-three rare elements, which, the speakers agreed, were all equally important and equally necessary in modern China.

On the third day of the conference, I was invited to speak. I began by remarking that the work of the conference might have been more efficiently accomplished if it had been held in a room less filled with tobacco smoke. Commenting on the previous speakers, I remarked that it was wrong to conclude that their institutes could handle all the elements, whatever they were, without considering the capacities of each establishment, the availability of the ore, and the demand for the product. For instance, platinum and other elements in the same group are extremely costly for China to continue buying abroad and paying for with the hard currency in her possession. On the other hand, such elements as indium and gallium still have too narrow an area of application to make processing in China worthwhile. I advised each institute to concentrate on three or four elements instead of spreading its efforts over the entire Mendeleyev Table, and to study thoroughly those elements and their compounds from the geochemical, analytical, and technological points of view.

I was followed on the rostrum by Comrade Tuh, the Academy's Party secretary, the man who had spent an entire day reporting on his trip to the Soviet Union. He thanked me, approved of what I had said, and assured me that the Academy would carefully study my suggestions. But it was only a moral victory, for my plan was quickly abandoned, like all the others.

At that conference, I discovered to my surprise that Chinese chemists don't understand their own chemical terminology, especially when it comes to the names of the elements. For 90 per cent of the elements, the Chinese have invented names that have absolutely no connection with those in international use—quite unsuitable one-syllable words, each of which has about a dozen homonyms—a vocabulary that results in indescribable confusion. One must admit that the task of developing a chemical terminology in Chinese is quite arduous, because of the ideograms—imagine the problem of representing tungsten or plutonium by means of an ideogram—so that, in this case as in many others, Chinese writing has had a retarding effect on the development of science. But in any case, I have become convinced that the Chinese seldom understand each other when it comes to the names of elements or of chemical compounds. Only when they adopt the international designations and write them in Russian or Latin characters (which some Chinese chemists now do, and they are the only ones who understand each other), will Chinese scientists be able to do serious work.

Science in China is organized on the Soviet model, and, as in the Soviet Union, the principal research takes place in special institutes rather than in universities or colleges.

The Chinese Academy of Sciences was founded in November, 1949; its first president was Kuo Mo-jo, a historian. The Academy was placed in charge of research institutes in Peking and in other cities too, where the Academy's local branch was the immediate authority. It also acquired a natural-sciences and a social-studies library. But there were many research groups, mainly in applied sciences, that came under the various ministries rather than the Academy.

The Academy's vast administrative apparatus was headed by the president and five vice-presidents. (Except for these six, the staff was composed, not of scientists and scholars, but of Party officials.) I met one of these dignitaries often, Woo Yu-hsun, the vice-president in charge of mathematics, physics, and chemistry. A lean, quick-moving, high-strung man who spoke excellent English (he had spent many years of study in America), he was a competent physicist and would have been a major one, had he not been snowed under by a continuous avalanche of papers—

the same drift of red tape under which all Chinese science lay buried. He no longer worked on his research but was engaged instead in "scientific planning" and was also kept busy "admitting" his past, present, and future errors at self-accusation meetings. Still, he seemed not to have lost the hope that better times were ahead, and that one day he could go back to research; he always appeared to be in an excellent mood.

I also met Comrade Wang Tao several times, the head of the foreign department of the Academy, and his assistant in charge of the Soviet section, a lady of thirty-five or so whom we shall call Madame Cheng, a lively and solidly built person.

Although the Academy administrators held many meetings and conferences at which research programs were discussed, their main role seemed to consist in transmitting government directives to the institutes. These directives were changed so often that the five vice-presidents never had time to supervise any scientific work, their time being wholly spent on what was always called "planning." As for President Kuo Mo-jo, he became a sort of decorative figure adorning official occasions, and of course, he often speechified at meetings.

Still and all, the Chinese could have accomplished very good scientific work, for their research laboratories were large and well equipped, even in comparison with Russia's. In pre-Revolutionary Russia, there had been few research institutions, most of them in St. Petersburg, under the Imperial Academy of Sciences; generally, research had been done at the universities, most of which had excellent laboratories. Then, after the Revolution, research institutes sprouted up all over the country, but, with rare exceptions, they did not have modern laboratories. Even to this day, most of the labs are located in the bare, grimy courtyards of old buildings in Moscow, Leningrad, or Kiev. Only recently did the

U.S.S.R. Academy of Sciences build new labs outside the former Moscow wall.

In China, the picture is very different. The universities built before 1949 in Peking, Nanking, and Kunming are located in beautiful country surroundings amid lawns, trees, and flowerbeds, and even the new research institutes are strikingly large and lavishly endowed with gardens and spacious grounds—so much the more remarkable in view of the shortage of arable land near China's major cities. (The discrepancy has lately been somewhat remedied by turning parts of the universities' land into truck gardens to supply the student cafeterias. Even so, the vegetable patches do not seriously mar the loveliness of these establishments, for they are always carefully screened with trees, bushes, and flowers.)

I had a number of contacts with scientists in the Academy's various branches and in other scientific bodies, aside from my work at the Chemistry Institute. Members of the Institute of Nonferrous Metals often came to consult me about their problems, and I had the opportunity to go to the Institute several times myself. As a consequence of my speech at the conference on rare elements, it was decided that my advice would be applied first in the field of platinum metals. A research group was formed at the Institute under the direction of Wang Li-cheng, an engineer who had been trained in the Soviet Union, and, between the two of us, we drew up a working program for it.

The Institute, situated in several rather large buildings and modern workshops, was one of the most impressive ones I had ever seen—at least in regard to its size—in either China or Russia. It was somewhat larger, in any case, than the Metallurgical Institute in Moscow, although about equal in the size of its staff—about 700 strong. But while in Moscow more than half of the scientists had doctorates or at least had done postgraduate work and were capable of independent research, in the Peking Institute, there were, I think, only about thirty persons with any advanced training, and those with experience in research could be counted on the fingers of one hand. Still, despite these deficiencies and thanks to their enthusiasm, the Peking Institute of Nonferrous Metals had done good work until 1958, their most successful efforts having been in their work on titanium, which is sometimes classified as a "rare element" because it occurs mostly in small quantities as an accessory in the ores of other metals. But in 1958, there as elsewhere, politics put an end to progress.

I was fairly well informed about this, because several visiting Soviet specialists were working at the Institute, and its members, especially the director, made frequent trips to the Soviet Union. I soon learned that for all practical purposes the Institute was paralyzed; the most shameless bluff was common practice; spectacular scientific "break-throughs" were often announced amid loud proclamations of Party spirit and patriotism when the achievements were in fact sheer fiction. As everywhere in China, there was much "research planning," but that was as far as the efforts went.

China's natural resources, in proportion to the size of her population, are dangerously meager, a fact that makes the efficient exploitation of them all the more important. A modern nation especially needs oil, but China is not rich in this precious resource: In recent years, her annual oil output has not exceeded 3 million tons, which is inadequate even if one allows for the low level of the country's economic development. To make up for this deficiency, efforts have been made to obtain liquid fuels from coal and to produce them by various synthetic methods. Research on these methods is done in the petroleum institutes of Peking and Dairen.

The Petroleum Institute of Peking asked me for advice on the composition of catalysts, and this gave me an opportunity to visit its premises and observe the way the scientists worked there. I was taken around the premises by a young Chinese engineer who spoke perfect Russian. (He had been adopted by the wife of a Russian priest from Harbin, who later had paid for his studies at the Harbin Polytechnic Institute.) From what he told me, I gathered that few of the technicians at the Petroleum Institute had had a university education, and that specialists in the field of synthetic liquid fuels were even scarcer.

Peking University, which was founded in 1898, has played an important role in the political as well as the cultural life of China. At the turn of the century, it was renowned for its writers and philosophers; and also it had at one time an assistant librarian who was destined to become the most famous man in China, one Mao Tse-tung. (The reform May Fourth Movement of 1919 also originated in the university.) By 1958, 10,000 students were studying in its twelve departments. The President, Ma Yin-ch'u, a well-known economist, was, I believe, the only prominent Chinese social scientist who had remained under the Communists. He was dismissed in 1960 for his "Malthusian views," which had come under attack during my first visit in 1958.

In February, 1958, I visited the university and was shown around by Huan Tzu-chin, of the physical chemistry department. The laboratories were spacious and well equipped, but, to my surprise, they were completely deserted, although we were there during regular working hours. I saw only four students during my whole tour, and those were not in a lab but playing a lively game of pingpong. Seeing my bewilderment, Professor Huan explained that many of the students had been sent out to do farm work, others were doing their tour of factory duty, and the rest were at a political meeting.

Scientific activity at the university began to decline, I was told, in the second half of 1957, and, by 1958, it had come to an almost complete stop.

It is impossible for me to give any account of my scientific activities in China in 1958 without saying a word about my interpreter, Chou Su-fen.

Su-fen looked a typical southern Chinese, with very brown skin and coal-black, slanting eyes. She dressed neatly and simply —in winter she wore navy-blue slacks and a warm, purple jacket; during the summer a dark skirt and light blouse. She was a quiet girl, always dignified, and she had only one weakness, tobacco, her fondness for which she tried always to hide from me. Although her name means "fragrant breeze," I would sometimes get the whiff of tobacco smoke as I entered my office in the mornings —she must have smoked a cigarette there before my arrival.

Su-fen was very gifted in calligraphy, and her Chinese ideograms were truly beautiful. She also dabbled in poetry and had studied chemistry and Russian. Apparently a convinced Communist, she was nevertheless touchingly naive; still, her intellectual qualities were mature and impressive—a lucid and precise mind, and a spirit that was both vivacious and disciplined. Su-fen also had a strange, stubborn streak of chauvinism and puritanism. She was, for instance, shocked when a visiting Russian expert married a Chinese girl whom he had met in the course of his work. The Russian, she explained to me, had deprived some Chinese man of a bride, and China had a considerable surplus of males. "He should have married a girl from Russia, where the situation is reversed," she said.

Once, on the blackboard at the entrance to the Institute, I saw Su-fen's neat and pretty ideograms disposed in twelve regular columns. It was a poem that began, "Look around you, Comrade, and see how good life has become, now that feudalism has been done away with." (But then, after a thief had climbed in at the window of her dormitory one night, causing a great commotion, Su-fen very seriously told me the next morning, "Well, you see, we have bad people, too.") For her, as for most Chinese of her generation, feudalism was a scapegoat for all the evils of the past. She once told me it was a feudal prejudice that prevented girls from swimming in her native town, Chengtu, on the Min River.

But Su-fen was, as I say, remarkably intelligent and able, and I often sought her advice not only on my lectures but also about how to formulate my answers to those who consulted with me, for I often risked offending a person by revealing to him how absurd or incongruous his question was. Su-fen would tactfully soften my replies if they sounded too abrupt to her, and it was she who advised me against advocating in public the modernization of Chinese chemical nomenclature, pointing out that although many Chinese would like to see that reform themselves, a foreigner's remarks on the subject might offend their patriotic feelings.

Su-fen worked with me throughout my stay in China in 1958, except during one trip I made to southern China. When I returned to the Soviet Union in August of that year, she came to see me off at the Peking airport, and that was the last time I saw her. When I returned to China in 1960, she was no longer in Peking: They had sent her to work in the country a few weeks before I arrived. Of all the young students and researchers I had ever known, little Su-fen was one of the most gifted and clever.

Su-fen worked with me on all my professional work, but Li Fu-teh was my personal interpreter and translator, and it is only fair that I mention him as well. I might point out here that I know full well that in mentioning him and several other individuals who were officially connected with me in my capacity as a Soviet specialist in China, I may endanger them or cause difficulty for them. I can only hope that such trouble as may arise will go no further than a small episode in a self-accusation meeting. I know that my Chinese friends have been taken to task at such meetings many times before—without having any connection with me, or, for that matter, without any fault on their part.

Now that relations between China and the Soviet Union have so seriously deteriorated, it is possible that the Chinese authorities will not judge me too severely for having fled the land of "revisionists and deviationists from true Marxism-Leninism." Besides, I have heard about Chinese reports on my activities in their country stating that my work was satisfactory and that they would have liked to invite me to come every year. Finally, the criticisms of China contained in this book are certainly not addressed to the persons who were officially connected with me during my stay in that country.

I think, therefore, that there is little reason to believe that the Chinese citizens I mention in this book by name, none of whom ever criticized the Chinese Communist regime in my presence, would be subjected to serious inconveniences on my account. They fulfilled their duties in regard to me, and that was all. As for those who indulged in forbidden frankness in their conversations with me, I left them unnamed, and what they told me I have only conveyed by hints such as "they say. . . ," or "I understand that. . . ."

Li Fu-teh performed his duties as my personal interpreter with scrupulous care and conscientiousness. I shared his services with another Soviet adviser, in organic chemistry, and Li strictly followed the instructions he had received on how to work with us, instructions he never mentioned to us and which I only learned about later from others. He was an honest, hard-working fellow who was loyal to his country and, I suppose, to her present rulers.

Li Fu-teh was about twenty-four—a rather tall, strapping fellow who had been graduated from the Russian Language Institute and was now attached to the Research Institute of Chemistry, where he was paid about 45 yüan a month, a salary that had to support not only Fu-teh and his wife but their little child.

Fu-teh was a great hand at managing to get things done; he knew *where* things could be bought and *what* was available—a talent that he applied with particular success to the business of finding good food, although the situation in Peking in 1958 limited the application of his abilities in this regard.

With his rather low salary, Li Fu-teh could not afford to dress well, but he was not interested in clothes in any case: What he longed for was a radio. He liked music—and had a rather good singing voice—and this only whetted his appetite for a small radio. The cheapest available cost about 100 yüan then, however, and all the time I knew him, a radio could be nothing more than a dream in his life.

CHAPTER THREE

Life in Peking

Despite all my work, I did my best to use my leisure hours in familiarizing myself with Chinese life and with the city of Peking. What seemed immediately apparent was that although entire sections of Peking were in no way different from districts of a European capital, the city was a unique metropolis.

In contrast to the layout of many cities, Peking's largest, highest buildings are on the outskirts, while within the city walls, low, one-story houses predominate, with a few odd, tall buildings sticking up among them like up-ended matchboxes. And the first thing to strike one on arriving there is the remarkable kinds of transport one uses to get about the city. Transportation systems from almost every century coexist in Peking—donkeys and horses, modern automobiles and buses. When I was in Peking, one saw automobiles primarily near the large hotels, and they were used exclusively by foreign tourists and specialists; even high-ranking Chinese officials only very rarely rode in them. The Chemistry Institute had one limousine, and I'm not sure that it wasn't shared with several of the Academy of Sciences' other establishments.

Chinese automotive plants produce only trucks, so the few cars there were in Peking were of foreign make, mostly Czechoslovak and Russian. The buses were always overcrowded because they were rare too, far rarer than in Leningrad, Moscow, or Kiev. A few taxis were stationed near the railroad station and near the main hotels. But to make up for this deficiency, there were thousands of bicycles, many more than in any Soviet town. Numerous pedicabs carried both goods and passengers (although there was plenty left in Peking for horses and donkeys to bear, and once, in the suburbs near the Institute, I even caught sight of a small caravan of camels); but pedicabs have not wholly displaced the ordinary rickshaws. There are still several hundred left in Peking, and I saw even more in other Chinese cities.

When I lived in Peking in the spring of 1958, there was a construction boom going on. Factories, offices, and schools, all of them covered with the typical Chinese bamboo scaffolding, were rising all over the city. In the suburbs near the Institute, an entire town in miniature had sprung up; more than fifty sizable houses —large square buildings, not pretty, but practical and comfortable—lodged the technicians and scientists who worked for the Academy institutes. They were separated, in classic Chinese fashion, by vegetable gardens, flower beds, and stands of trees, and in this respect resembled the areas of Peking where the *fantsi*, the classic Chinese one-story, rectangular houses with windows and doors giving onto the same side, are interspersed with fields and small gardens. Sometimes, two or three of them will share an interior courtyard, turning their blind walls to the outside world.

For the research workers, technicians, and scientists working in Peking, I should say that housing conditions were not worse, perhaps even better than in Moscow. Yet the population is growing fast, despite the measures taken to slow down the city's growth:

The peasants who arrive from the country in search of food and employment are periodically rounded up and sent back to their villages.

Once, while driving me on an errand, Li Fu-teh asked my permission to make a detour to pick up some belongings an aunt of his had given him. When the limousine stopped at her small house, the little old lady emerged and, following the old Chinese tradition of hospitality, insisted that I come in too, to pay her a visit and share a cup of tea. Li Fu-teh explained that I would be more comfortable waiting in the car, for his instructions specifically forbade him to invite his Soviet charges into any Chinese home without prior authorization. But the aunt was adamant: The tradition of hospitality must be honored. She threatened, I gather, to withhold the belongings if her nephew broke that tradition, so, at the risk of incurring the ire of his employers, Fu-teh complied with his aunt's desire.

The old woman opened the door (there was no lock on it) and motioned me inside. Her house was a single room, about 12 feet square, and I was charmed by its cleanliness and by its pretty and tasteful appointments. Against one wall was a wide Chinese bed, near another, a round table, an armoire, a few chairs, and the stove. For this room, the old lady paid 4 yüan a month. In the summer, she lived with a friend outside the city, and Li Fu-teh told me that she intended to move to another, better room soon, for which she would pay 6 or 8 yüan a month.

Now in Moscow, a woman like that, living on a pension, would consider herself exceptionally lucky to have such a room. I still remember well the late A. G. Rastryopina, who worked at the Institute in Moscow, and who died at the age of seventy-two without ever having lived in a room of her own, having waited for thirty years in one dormitory or another.

It was quite a general practice to live in the suburbs of Peking and travel several hours to get to work. Some people lived in dormitories, where the worst threat was bedbugs. These disgusting insects had managed to survive all the successive campaigns to destroy them, including the "Campaign against the Four Evils," in which they took over the sparrows' role as Public Enemy Number One when the latter had been posthumously rehabilitated. Perhaps they were saved by their color—a revolutionary red.

Li Fu-teh himself lived with his wife and child in a somewhat larger room than his aunt occupied. Almost half of it was taken up by the enormous bed, next to which stood the baby's crib. Next to the door, a few shelves contained books and the small bags of the family's rice and flour rations. Two small tables and chairs completed the furnishings. Across the hall, there was a kitchen with a stove big enough for one kettle or pot at a time (the fuel for which was coal dust packed into balls). The authorities had promised Li another room in the same apartment for his mother, who was coming to Peking to look after the baby.

When I returned to Peking in 1960, Sino-Soviet relations had begun to deteriorate, and the mutual distrust between Russians and Chinese was in the open. Despite my excellent relations with Chinese co-workers and the directors of the Institute where I worked, none of them ever invited me to his home (although many of them came to see me at my hotel), due to the instructions they had received on how to treat Soviet experts—although two years before, in 1958, I had visited the three-room apartment where Professor Liu, his wife, and two sons were then living.

As one drives through the streets of central Peking, one sees in almost every quarter the high, golden roofs of the temples, hidden behind encircling walls. Here and there, one finds beautiful old buildings with their guardian stone lions, marble terraces and balustrades along the canals, magnificent gates and arches of elaborately carved wood. Peking is like one enormous museum, with the exhibits dispersed in parks, behind walls, in palaces and houses in all parts of the city. The wonderful Wall of Dragons, for instance, stands in a garden at the end of a remote alley. I visited some of the palaces, most of which are grouped together in the old Imperial and Forbidden Cities. The high, cold, dark rooms with their low furniture seemed unattractive and uncomfortable, and I wondered how people could ever have lived in them in winter. Because they are so dark, the old palaces are unsuitable for museums, and more recent Chinese buildings seem more cheerful, better arranged, and more inviting—like the Peking municipal library.

One of the most beautiful monuments of old Peking is the Temple of Heaven, a round, fairly high, but beautifully proportioned structure with a three-tiered roof, which stands alone on a small incline. Next to it is the Wall of Echoes, where words spoken quite softly toward one part of the wall can be heard diametrically opposite. Next to the temple is a square approached by steps with carved stone balustrades and a parapet. This square forms a harmonious whole with the temple, but a dissonant note is introduced into the scene by the tents of an army camp spread out in a grove below, and by the columns of marching soldiers. It is said that the Temple of Heaven was dedicated, not to war, but to man's most peaceful pursuit—agriculture. In imperial China, emperors offered prayers for a good crop here. But the contemporary "emperor" of China gives more attention to the sword than to the ploughshare.

I visited a number of Buddhist temples in Peking and other Chinese cities. Although they vary in style, size, and surroundings, they are all built according to the same oblong or square plan, divided in two parts. To the right of the sacred statues of Buddha and his disciples there always hangs a bell, and on the left

stands a large drum. I got into the habit of striking these bells
lightly with a coin to ascertain of what metals they were made.
Nowadays, bells are seldom made of solid copper but usually of
an alloy of tin, copper, and zinc. (There is even a term for it,
"bell alloy.") But any "pure" copper obtained before the process
of electrolytic purification was introduced—that is, before the
late nineteenth century—will contain other metals as well, and the
greater the amount of these other metals, the older the bell
probably is. The work done by Professor Chung in Hangchow,
for example, in the analysis of old Chinese metal objects, has
revealed fascinating information in this field and is worth every
encouragement, for it will lead to interesting results not only for
metallurgists but for historians and other persons interested in
the culture of China.

In the center of Peking, along the banks of a chain of artificial
lakes, there is still another park. The Mortar, a tall, white tower
with neither windows nor doors, apparently a Buddhist shrine,
stands on a hill in the middle; there are arbors and paths to stroll
along, and fishermen and boaters on the lakes. On May Day, the
top Party leaders, Premier Chou En-lai, and other members of the
cabinet attend the fireworks display, when rockets and flares are
sent up from boats on the lakes.

In northwest Peking, there is still another park—the Summer
Palace park, just beyond the university and the new scientific
buildings. But this park is fairly recent, since it was laid out during
the reign of the next to last Manchu ruler, the Dowager Empress
Tzu Hsi.

Despite the lakes on the grounds of the Summer Palace and
despite the artificial ponds, despite all the canals and the river some
ten miles away where the beautiful Marco Polo bridge com-
memorates that famous traveler, Peking has no river of its own,
and no natural, convenient water supply. During the spring and

summer of 1958, the Peking newspapers devoted a great deal of space to news about the construction of a dam and reservoir on a river about thirty miles north of Peking. (The site was near the tombs of the thirteen Ming emperors.)

Each institute or organization in Peking, each higher-educational institution, sent its members to work at the reservoir for a week or two. At the end of May, when the meeting of the Central Committee of the Chinese Communist Party had ended, the entire Committee also drove to the construction site of the dam; the newspapers were full of reports of their devoted and successful efforts. Some articles told of the lady Minister of Health running from one VIP to another and beseeching them to spare their health; there were descriptions of Mao straining under a yoke laden with two buckets of earth, together with pictures to document the feat; Chou En-lai, the newspapers reported enthusiastically, stayed behind for a few days, living in barracks with the workers and sharing their food. Exactly a week later, I too drove out to the dam, where about 100 members of the Chemistry Institute were then doing their share of work.

The wide road approaching the dam was all torn up, and people were moving busily about the site. When I came closer, I saw that some of them were pushing small cars on narrow-gauge rails. Along the crest of a long, low levee—the future dam—groups of men and women were laboring. I recognized some familiar faces from the Institute: Tao, who was always ready for an argument over scientific projects; the three young women, bosom friends—Su Sao-bai, who was dark and pretty, Chang Bin, a pleasant girl who had been educated in America, and the bespectacled, good-humored Lu Chen-yi.

Someone gave me a spade, and I began to load one of the cars with earth. Near me, three men operated together, one man digging and the other two hoisting a large spade by means of some sort of pulley, but this cooperative system did not seem very efficient. Every other moment, Lu Chen-yi rushed up to me begging me not to overstrain myself.

In the meantime, a whole crowd of people had gathered behind the earthen barrier near where I worked. Holding their spades like rifles, they stood at attention and watched me work. I went on digging, and the crowd around me kept on growing: The loud-speakers had announced that such-and-such a Soviet specialist had arrived to work at the construction site. The announcement was followed by a list of my titles and degrees and a few compliments about my ardent desire to help China develop her sciences and my worthy contribution to the great national effort. Inasmuch as I had not really paid any attention to Lu Chen-yi's exhortations to spare myself, Hua Shao-chun came to me half an hour later and began to explain how important it was to conserve the precious health of visiting Soviet specialists, since they played such a supreme role in China's building of socialism. So, when evening came, I bid good-by to my Institute friends and left the construction site.

Soon after, the dam was formally dedicated and opened. The ground around it was still raw and torn up, but, on the whole, the dam itself was finished. On top of the dam, a group of us Soviet specialists stood, together with a brass band and officiating dignitaries. Ice-cream vendors were busy preparing their merchandise (which, to be exact, were artificially colored ices slightly sweetened with saccharine, and not real ice cream at all). Down below the dam, a yellow square of soldiers were surrounded by a mass of blue-clad men and women. At a distance, I could see a large hill and on a plateau, the construction workers' barracks.

Then the speeches began. There were ardent praises of Mao—the inspiration of the dam, the builder of the New China; there were eulogies of the dam itself; speaker after speaker hailed the significance of a dam that would stave off the spring floods and irrigate several thousand acres of soil; due tribute was also paid to the enthusiasm of those who had joined in the construction "voluntarily."

I know full well that the few spadefuls of earth I shovelled from one heap to another had only propaganda value, if any at all. But it occurred to me that my going there had been a welcome opportunity for hundreds of workers to take a little rest, if nothing else. I had observed that the workers hardly strained themselves, though, to say the least; and I am sure that two or three hundred men with excavators and trucks could have done the work much faster and more cheaply than the tens of thousands of "enthusiastic volunteers" who had to be transported, billeted, and fed for weeks on end. At the same time, the Chemistry Institute and others like it could have gone on with their regular work, without wasting all that time on a token effort of manual labor.

One of the first things that struck me about Peking were its hundreds of little shops and boutiques. In Moscow, where, as all over the Soviet Union, private enterprise does not exist, there are primarily the large government stores; in Peking, however, there are few large shops, and the traditional small family ones have simply been nationalized, their owners transformed into "government managers." These shopkeepers continued to live and do their business in the same quarters, and the business of buying and selling remained, by and large, en famille.

An abundance of little shops did not mean, however, an abundance of goods. (In Moscow, despite the fewer stores and the shortcomings of the Soviet production and distribution systems, the figure of available consumer goods per capita of the population was far more favorable than in Peking.) The shopkeepers were, in fact, in a tragic situation. Their average annual income was fixed at about 5 per cent of the net value of their stock and equipment at the time of the nationalization, and, since goods were cheap, this was virtually no income at all. The only prospering shops were those near the tourist hotels or those where luxury goods were sold.

In general, I would say that there were simply more shops in Peking than the city's population could support, and consequently, the stores were very often short on merchandise. I remember going into one obscure little shop that seemed to have almost no goods at all—the shopkeeper was thin and pale, with two sickly small children. I bought a pencil-box from him, with a picture on it of Chinese schoolchildren reading and doing chemical experiments; I have it still, in Canada. Each time I look at it, I see that street again, the miserable little shop, and those abjectly suffering and dignified people.

There was one large department store on Wang Fu-tzin Street, where some basic goods and certain luxury items were available. Cotton yard goods and clothes were sold only by coupons, and the yearly ration per person in 1958 was about three yards; by 1960, this had been cut in half. Handkerchiefs and towels, however, could be obtained without coupons, and woolen and silk goods as well. It was possible to buy a ready-made or custom suit to order, or to choose from the store's wide variety of furs, enamelware (in particularly great demand in Moscow, where people will queue up for it), watches, jewelry, and embroidered silk pictures—the latter mostly landscapes or portraits of the Marxist saints, Marx, Engels, Lenin, Stalin, and Mao (I found no portrait of Khrushchev). There was also a plentiful supply of cheap canvas shoes and of rather pretty writing paper and envelopes.

The only foodstuffs on sale in the department store were candy and tea, but there were also, of course, special tea shops where one could find a staggering variety of different teas at various prices. There were other specialty shops—greengrocers, butchers, poultry shops—but I never found a bakery in all of Peking. There were also small workshops with carpenters, glass blowers, tin-smiths, etc., and on almost every street, there was a tailor. It is nowhere near so complicated to have a suit custom-made in Peking as in Moscow; consequently, many tailors thrived on their business with the visiting Soviet specialists; one would often see their street signs written in Russian.

In a special section of Peking's market, works of art and antiques were sold, but a national law forbids the sale to foreigners of any antique more than 100 years old.

There is one striking difference between Chinese and Soviet consumer goods: The Chinese products are usually much prettier. The Chinese people have a fine aesthetic awareness for the harmonies of form and color, no matter what their background or education. One sees the proof of this everywhere in China, in the interior decoration of the most humble room or in the architecture of her national monuments. It reminded me of the Ukrainian people, who for many centuries have cultivated their love of beauty in nature and in everyday life.

It appears that the shoppers of Peking are not particularly afraid of pickpockets or thieves. Many of the visiting Russians accounted for the small number of thefts by the severity of Chinese prisons, which, it was said, would cripple a man in six months, whereas the saying is that "in Soviet jails, hooligans and thieves grow fat." In any case, it was quite a contrast, for Muscovites know that, in their city, there are tens of thousands of thefts each year.

One never sees dogs in the streets of Peking, because all the dogs were exterminated in 1957. During my entire stay in Peking, I saw only one, I believe, and that beyond the city limits. The extermination may seem to have been a rather drastic measure; I gathered from a French translation of a Chinese text that Peking dogs had been a friendly lot: "Three miracles can be observed in Peking: The dogs do not bite, the horses do not kick, and the young girls can walk safely in the streets." But it was considered necessary, since dogs were "no longer required in view of the lack of thieves." This was the official explanation, but I am quite convinced that some of man's best friends wound up in a stewpot, for it is an open secret that dog flesh was a staple food in China. One Chinese proverb says that "a sheep's head on a butcher's sign does not mean that dog meat is not sold within." I am sure the wise man who coined that phrase never suspected how accurately it would one day describe a historic period in the life of China—the period of the building of socialism under the leadership of that genius, Mao.

CHAPTER FOUR

The Friendship Hotel and the Soviet Embassy: Sino-Soviet Cooperation in Peking

I have never yet come across a description—indeed, I have never seen mentioned—one of the most interesting places in all of Peking, a place I would describe as a monument to the short-lived honeymoon of Soviet-Chinese relations. This monument is the Hotel Druzhba—the Friendship Hotel. It is actually much more than a hotel: It is a huge complex of buildings with rooms and restaurants, stores and workshops, even a theater, a school, gymnasiums, cinemas, and parks. I do not know when the Friendship Hotel was built, but I can say for certain that it was already operating in 1956 and probably earlier. From that time until 1960, when the last Soviet specialists left, five or six thousand Soviet scientists, engineers, and technicians must have lived there, together with their wives and children, for periods ranging from three months to two years and sometimes even longer. Truly a remarkable institution, and yet I think that the falsity of Sino-Soviet friendship has nowhere been made so obvious as in the hotel dedicated to it.

The central building of the Friendship Hotel is a huge, seven-story gray edifice with an enormous staircase leading up to the entrance. Behind this are four houses of about the same size and a theater. The central building housed those Soviet specialists who had come to China for only a few months, while those who came for longer lived in the buildings in back.

Behind the theater stood the kitchen and two large dining rooms, which one could reach via the glass-enclosed passages without having to go into the street. There were greenhouses, buildings where visitors from other Communist countries were lodged, and yet another dining room for these visitors. The school for Soviet children was also located on the premises, together with a tennis court and indoor swimming pool. (Classes at the school were conducted in Russian—indeed, the Chinese language was not even taught—but a few Chinese children did attend.)

By the entrance gate to the hotel grounds, a sentry was posted to whom all pedestrians had to show passes before being let in, although those in cars could pass unchecked.

The rooms in the Friendship Hotel were large, comfortably furnished, airy, and light. They were cleaned every day but Sunday, usually by two men working together. I used to leave my entire monthly salary, which represented roughly what one of them would earn in ten months, in my room, but I never missed a fen, nor did I ever hear of a theft in any of the rooms. Once, though, in 1957, a Soviet expert missed his watch, and another couldn't find his camera, and there was a terrible to-do. The hotel management organized typical self-accusation meetings for the Chinese staff, but none of the employees confessed. The Russians continued to suspect the room personnel, but a few days later, the hotel management showed them a photograph of a Soviet expert's teenage son trying to sell the watch and camera to an employee of a Peking store. The incident was closed when the delinquent young man was sternly requested to return to the Soviet Union forthwith, together with his father and all other members of his family.

Like all Soviet specialists, I and one of my colleagues had a limousine at our disposal that we used to go to and from work, for shopping expeditions, a visit in the country, to go to the theater, etc. The name of our driver was Chang Hua-shen, and we became good friends. He was an amusing young man, clever and resourceful, and very good company. As I came to know him better, I learned that he came from northern China and had fought in the Korean War, where he had picked up some Russian from the Soviet troops he had met there—although, as everyone knows, Russians did not take part in that war. (It was said in Russia that the Peking government avoided an international incident when decorating Soviet air force men by turning Vaniouchine into Wang Yu-chin, Sinitsin into Sin Yi-tzin, etc.) Whenever I got into the car, he would cry, *"Poyekhali!"* ("Off we go!") and we would roar off.

While waiting for me at the Institute or at the hotel in the evenings, he was always reading some Chinese book or other; once, I asked him if he knew all the ideograms or whether he still came across some that were unfamiliar.

"It happens," he said cheerfully. "There're usually one or two on each page I don't recognize, but I can make out what they mean from the context."

Hua-shen, like all the other drivers attached to the Friendship Hotel (I gathered there were about 750 of them in 1957, but the number gradually decreased), was fed in the hotel cafeteria and had to report regularly at prescribed hours. I don't know how he managed it, but he was always ready and waiting whenever I appeared in need of the car. Hua-shen was also very popular among his confrères and with the management, and the authorities evidently thought highly enough of him to offer him a job at one of China's embassies abroad, a gesture of confidence which would have placed him in a very favorable position but which he refused because he did not want to leave his mother. Every evening, and sometimes during the day, he went to political meetings to receive his daily inoculation of revolutionary enthusiasm, but obedient as he was, he could not disguise his apprehension of the commandment to work for a stint in the country. When he was eventually sent out of Peking for a few weeks, he was almost sick with worry.

"Aren't you pleased to be going to the country?" I asked him.

"I have to be pleased," he said desolately. But he was horrified because he had heard from other chauffeurs that he would be badly fed, that, indeed, he would see nothing on his table but cereal.

I always ate breakfast and lunch in the hotel restaurant; my supper, which consisted of bread, fruit, and tea, I took in my room. The fruit was wonderfully varied—apples and pears, exotic lichees and mangoes which I had never tasted or even seen before. I was to appreciate this plentiful supply of fruit two years later when I worked in subtropical Kunming, where I found it impossible to get even an apple or pear and only once, just before my departure, managed to find peaches. I could occasionally get bananas in Kunming, but that was all. (Yet at much the same time, China had signed an agreement with the Soviet Union to deliver half a million tons of apples to her "socialist ally," and apples were being sold in Siberian towns that had rarely even seen them before.) In Peking, I had pineapples, bananas, peaches, plums, grapes, watermelons, cantaloupes, lichees, tangerines— every imaginable fruit and all of them very cheap.

One could buy all sorts of food in the hotel—white and dark bread, sugar, butter, salami, and pickled cucumbers. These last two, of course, were usually eaten with alcoholic beverages— wines as well as brandy and liquors. But the stores where these things were sold catered exclusively to foreign visitors; Chinese had no access to them, not even our Chinese interpreters.

There were two dining rooms at the hotel on either side of the theater. At both, a menu on each table offered a choice of Russian or Chinese dishes, all of which could be ordered for a ridiculously low price: one and one-half yüan (about 60 cents) for an enormous repast served by helpful and friendly waitresses. There was also a bar at one end of the room where one could get vodka, beer, wine, and meat tarts and sandwiches to go with the drinks. A third dining room catered primarily to non-Soviet foreigners, whom one could easily distinguish by their dress. Li Fu-teh once pointed out a tall, pleasant-looking fellow in rather narrow trousers and a beige jacket. "He's a Canadian specialist," he explained. The menu in that dining room included German and other West European dishes, although one could also order a Chinese dinner there.

The two dining rooms for Soviet personnel were, as a rule, most crowded in the evenings, when everyone had dinner with their families or in large groups. Then, almost always, late in the evening, clusters of somewhat inebriated men would emerge from the dining rooms and, walking rather unsteadily, would return to their rooms where they often went on drinking late into the night. When I left for work in the morning, I would notice that rows and rows of empty bottles stood by the doors of certain rooms that were being cleaned; the battery of bottles was especially impressive on Monday mornings.

For myself, I was content with a small glass of wine or a bottle of beer, which I usually shared with Li Fu-teh, but my relative abstemiousness incurred the disapproval of some of my compatriots when I refused to take part in the drinking bouts they conducted in their rooms.

Now it so happened that a confidential circular was issued by the Central Committee of the C.P.S.U. in the spring of 1958: "Reference: Combatting Drunkenness." It reached Peking two months later, and the small Party cell in Peking of which I was a member was instructed to convey its orders to all its members and to punish the wrongdoers. But in Peking, far from home, our Party zeal had considerably diminished; there were only twelve of us in that cell, all scientists, and most of us Party members only out of necessity. We were supposed to hold meetings once or twice a month, but we had reduced the number of convocations to a minimum. Anyway, at one such meeting, we had to discuss the subject of drunkenness because a cell member had been denounced for it by a clerk in the Soviet Consulate in Shanghai. At home, the discussion would have ended with the "discovery" of the scapegoat, who would have been offered up in sacrifice to placate the Central Committee and to demonstrate the zeal of the Party cell. But, since we were abroad and less sensitive to immediate pressure to prove that we were "heeding the directive from above," we decided not to sacrifice our drinking comrade. I, being a chemist, suggested that the state of extreme prostration in which he had been found could be explained by the various admixtures in the inferior Chinese liquors, none of which, of course, existed "in the government-controlled vodka sold in our beloved Soviet Fatherland." Our resolution said: "Don't drink, but if you do, go home and do it privately in your own room."

One Soviet expert assured me that in one Chinese province (I believe it was Shantung), the natives drank just as much as Russians do. I should think, though, that, on the whole, Chinese drink considerably less than my fellow countrymen or Europeans in general, and that they rather disapproved of the drinking bouts that went on in the Friendship Hotel.

One of the favorite distractions offered at the hotel was the weekly Saturday night dance. I did not really enjoy this sort of thing, but unfortunately, my room was right over the dance hall, so whether I liked it or not, I had to suffer through an entire night of the most frightful noise; the drums, violins, trumpets, and shouts outdid even the worst moments of the campaign against the Peking sparrows. The wives of Russian specialists adored these dances, for it gave them a wonderful opportunity to dress up, chat, and weave their little intrigues. For the bachelors, there were young Chinese women students who came regularly to the Saturday night celebrations.

In exasperation and out of curiosity, I finally decided to go to one of these dances: The hall was indeed very crowded, very noisy, and very lively. A number of the women seemed to be having a wonderful time—some of them were downright flirts—but the husbands remained relatively quiet and morose. My impression of this general pattern was verified later in the night, when I was awakened at about three o'clock by a bang in the next room and a man's voice saying in Russian: "Who was that man you were dancing with when I came in? I'm telling you, as soon as I'm out of sight you try to make a fool of me! How can I work with you carrying on like this? . . ." And on and on in the same vein. I couldn't go back to sleep that night, and in the morning, I asked to be given another room. Ten days later, I moved to quarters far away from the dance hall.

I came to realize, however, that such scenes were a common occurrence in the Friendship Hotel, and this was no surprise, for a most peculiar atmosphere prevailed in that establishment.

As a rule, scientists and specialists coming to Peking for more than six months brought their families along with them. This practice was encouraged by the Soviet authorities, who wanted to avoid too much intimacy between the Soviet specialists and the Chinese. (When I first talked with the official at the Soviet Embassy who looked after Soviet citizens in China, he gravely warned me about the "dangerously artful" Chinese women.) In any case, while the Soviet specialists were out each day on their jobs and the children were in school, the wives stayed at home in the Friendship Hotel, and naturally they had nothing to keep themselves occupied with. They did not have to cook, to wash or to iron, or even to clean their rooms. Of course they could read, but although I was a regular visitor to the Druzhba library, where I spent many hours, I never saw any Soviet woman there. (The only Soviet citizens I saw in the library were twelve- or fourteen-year-old children.)

What *did* the Soviet women do? They went out on excursions, went to theaters and the movies either in the hotel or in town, took various "cures"—mostly for imaginary ills, making wide use of Chinese medicine, including the "needle treatment," or acupuncture—and, like idle women all over the world, they visited one another. Most of all, of course, they went shopping, in the department store, in the Chinese markets, or on Wang Fu-tzin Street, where there were shops that catered especially to their tastes.

All this was true of the women who did not work themselves, who were in China only as a part of the family of some invited Soviet specialist. The Russian women scientists and technicians—geologists, engineers, etc.—who came to China with us worked just as hard and well as the men; one could reproach them only for their weakness for clothes; but then, they did not go in for heavy drinking as a rule.

Most Soviet specialists in China were paid roughly 520–40 yüan a month, in addition to their regular pay for their work in Russia, which was continued while they were away and paid into their accounts in the Soviet Union. I, for instance, in my capacity as head of a laboratory in Moscow, continued to receive 5,000 old rubles a month (a salary that, even allowing for taxes and other inevitable charges, was five times that of a skilled worker), of which 60 per cent was paid into my account back home. At the same time, I received 530 yüan a month in China. At the official exchange rate, one yüan was worth two old rubles, but in purchasing power, it was worth more: In reports on the Chinese national economy, Soviet economists placed the purchasing power of one yüan at about six old rubles. It was at an unofficial rate of ten rubles to a yüan that we bought Chinese money from one another. As a rule, it was the married men who were always short of Chinese currency, because of their wives' shopping sprees.

For their part, the Soviet authorities in China did their best to channel at least part of the Chinese money we received into their treasury, for the Soviet Union badly wanted Chinese currency. Thus, in the Russian bookstore at the hotel, we could buy certain Russian books that were quite unobtainable back home—even though they were Soviet editions—but we had to pay in yüan. The inhabitants of the Friendship Hotel were less interested in books, however, than in other purchasable items—television sets, refrigerators, and, above all, automobiles. All these things could be paid for, in Peking, in yüan, to be obtained on one's return to the Soviet Union. The prices were reckoned on a special rate of exchange somewhat more favorable than the official one but not as good as our "free exchange."

The most alluring bait was the automobile. To get a car in Russia, people had to put their names on a list and then wait at least a couple of years for their turn to come up. There were all sorts of inconveniences—guarantees, checks, etc. In Peking, on the other hand, the whole procedure was delightfully simple: You paid, got a receipt, and when you returned home to Russia, all you had to do was present the receipt at a depot for new cars and pick one out for yourself. However, few of the Russians who came to China bought cars, since most of their Chinese cash went toward their wives' purchases—cheap furs, china, silks, dresses. Only the bachelors tried to save enough for a car.

Given the strange, isolated quality of life at the Druzhba, it was natural that certain problems were a continual headache for the hotel's management, problems that were, in fact, never adequately solved. Among these, the problem of the Soviet children was paramount. Cut off from the world around them, from the homes where they had grown up and from their natural milieu, living in the most artificially imposed conditions, the young sons and daughters of the Soviet technicians were existing in an atmosphere that was far from conducive to a healthy childhood or adolescence. The hotel management had enough on their hands with the simple job of keeping the mothers occupied; no one knew how to keep the children entertained. Visits to the theater or cinema were multiplied in vain—it was shopping sprees that remained the most popular way of wasting an afternoon. In any event, it might have been expected that a number of children would become restless and spoiled to the point of delinquency. The boy who stole the camera was not atypical, and the girls spent their time in gossiping and in busily doing nothing.

On one occasion, the Party bureau sent me to talk to the graduating class at the school for Soviet children about the problems of choosing a future career. As usual, my visit began with a desperate search for the official in charge, hopefully the principal, who could not be found. When I finally did encounter some such authority, I was shocked to discover that the education of

Soviet children had been entrusted to such a crude and unattractive person.

Still, in all, the hotel management did a remarkable job in providing entertainment to fill the leisure hours of the Russian visitors and their families. In the halls leading to the dining rooms, colorful posters announced plays and films, tours to interesting spots around Peking, visits to factories producing items of ladies' wear and adornment. There were excursions every day, it seemed, and weekdays and holidays were indistinguishable for the Friendship Hotel ladies, just as the distinction between day and night tends to be lost during an arctic summer. Somehow, though, the ladies tired of doing nothing during the week and so had to have their rest on Sunday too. The theater at the hotel was constantly active as well. Then, on various holidays such as Soviet Armed Forces Day, on February 23, or International Woman's Day, on March 8, we were offered performances by Chinese professional actors and Soviet amateurs. It goes without saying that major holidays like May Day were marked by spectacles and entertainments both at the hotel and elsewhere in the city. Lastly, the specialists who stayed in China for a year or more were able to spend their vacations at a resort on the shore of the Gulf of Po Hai and relatively close to Peking.

There were other, more serious ways of spending the leisure hours. Groups met regularly to study Chinese, discuss international policy, etc. But the library and reading room were not too popular with my colleagues or their families. It is worth noting that this library—designed especially to cater to thousands of Russian-speaking persons who were living in China and who were therefore likely to be interested in the history, geography, and cultural life of that country—contained only one book treating these matters: a pamphlet-reprint of the article on China from the *Soviet Encyclopedia*. There was not a single Russian- or

English-language magazine devoted to China or Chinese affairs or published in China. Perhaps to make up for this, newspapers and magazines published in Russia were well represented. But I think this paucity of material on China indicates in some way how much the vaunted Sino-Soviet friendship was really worth. I should add, though, that, in downtown Peking, there were several large bookstores where one could buy a wide variety of technical books in Russian and English. I found some English-language books there on history and philosophy that would never have been allowed in the Soviet Union.

From time to time, the Soviet cultural attaché in Peking organized lectures at the hotel or Embassy on economic and political themes. At one of these, he described China's economic difficulties and expressed mild dissent with certain Chinese economic policies. He pointed out that, unlike the situation in the Soviet Union, where goods are kept in state-owned storehouses, individual stores in China must allocate and stock reserves of goods: Thus, the very foundation of the Chinese currency's purchasing power is unreliable.

While the Chinese management of the Friendship Hotel occupied itself with the material, bodily needs of the Soviet citizens in Peking, maintaining our morale and patriotic ardor was a task entrusted entirely to the enormous staff of the Soviet Embassy, from the ambassador down to the myriad agents of the MVD. The duties of this horde of parasites were naturally lightened by the fact that, unlike the situation in a capitalist country, a Soviet citizen in China who wanted to defect had nowhere to go, for, at that time, the Chinese did not grant asylum to defectors from the Soviet Union, as they did to those from Yugoslavia. But, because of this, the security agents who dominated the Embassy staff held Soviet citizens in as tight a grasp as they did back in Russia. It was all done on the quiet, without any noise, but the power and, shall I say, the arrogance of the Embassy staff in Peking nevertheless was amply evident from time to time. I must say, in all my life, during all my bitter experiences with the bureaucracy of the Soviet state, I seldom encountered such a collection of incapable idlers, such a complete lack of discipline, or such scorn and callous rudeness to Soviet citizens as I did in the Soviet Embassy, and particularly the Consulate, in Peking. How many times did we have to wait for days on end to find the right little official for some simple red-tape job!

A few days after I first arrived in Peking, I went to register at the Consulate, which was in a two-story house next to the Embassy. In the waiting room, ill-lit and disgustingly messy, where torn, dirty, and out-of-date Soviet magazines were flung in an untidy pile on a low table, there was not a soul to be seen, neither visitor nor clerk. A greasy cardboard sign was pinned to a door leading to a side room: It announced that the Consulate was open twice a week for two hours. Wondering what our consular employees did with themselves on the other five days, I made a point of going back punctually at the time the office hours began. I knocked at the door of the reception room but no one answered, although I could hear voices. I turned the handle, opened the door, and walked in.

Two men were standing at the desk, deeply immersed in conversation.

"Good morning, comrades," I said, but they ignored me. I had nothing to do but to stand and take a good look at them. At last, about five minutes later, one of the two men glanced at me with an irritated look and barked, "What d'you want?"

I handed him my passport. "I've come to register."

He took it, casually riffled through it, and tossed it across the desk to his companion. "Here, register that!"

The other fellow opened a ledger, jotting something down, and studied my documents. He tossed the passport back to me and dismissed me curtly. "That'll be all."

My next visit to the Embassy occurred several weeks later, when, as I had been instructed in Moscow, I went to the Soviet cultural attaché's office. I was received at the Embassy (once I had gotten past the heavily guarded gate) by a smiling Chinese guide—the only man I ever saw smile in the Soviet Embassy—who showed me the way to the office I intended to visit. As it turned out, I had quite a difficult time locating the particular official I wanted, but the third time around, I found him in his office—a thick-set, almost completely bald man staring at the world through large round glasses. Behind his superficial politeness, I sensed certain familiar qualities; he was like a mixture of a MVD agent and a small-town economic boss. He nodded as I entered and gestured me to a chair, then resumed the rather animated conversation he had been engaged in when I entered. I gathered that he and his visitor were arguing about a sum of money connected with someone's travel allowance.

Finally, when the young man left, Comrade A. turned to me. He asked me about my work, inquired whether I was comfortable at the Friendship Hotel, and, continuing in his dry, monotonous voice, warned me of the dangers of associating with young Chinese women, offering counsels of wisdom on how to resist temptations of the flesh. Surely he must have realized that I needed the sermon less than he, and that common sense would tell him that at my age, I was not in any great danger. But then, he was just doing his routine job.

Suddenly, he looked up from the forms I had filled out and given him, and, glaring at me, said abruptly, "Did you see that shyster?"

"Pardon?" I asked, nonplussed.

"That faker who was just in here?" Without waiting for an

answer, he went on, "Just think, the son-of-a-bitch is supposed to have come here to help out Chinese journalists!" He screwed up his mouth and changed his voice as he uttered these last words, apparently trying to imitate the young man who had been with him when I arrived. "The Chinese need him like a fish needs an umbrella. And to us, he's about as useful as a he-goat to a milkman. Imagine, that parasite, that good-for-nothing, thinks he doesn't get paid enough. Well, you're quite a different case, of course, you're a doctor, you're a professor, and you have a decoration, but still, you work like a dog and are satisfied with 530 yüan a month, aren't you? That lazy slob gets 650 a month for doing exactly nothing, and he's mad, comes here, and asks for a raise. What reasons does he give? He's been junketing all over China for no purpose at all."

Comrade A. kept on with his stream of invective against his previous visitor. "Tass sent that guy here," he said, "ostensibly to teach journalism to the Chinese. Well, it seems to me they can manage very well without his help."

"So why was he sent?" I asked quietly.

"Why!" repeated Comrade A., irritated. "Simply because there's an agreement. A specialist in such-and-such a field is needed. Who do you send? One man marked 'Journalist.' It's like a cat in a sack—how can you guess what his color, sex, or temperament is, whether he's a good mouser or just a lazy fat animal. . . ."

Comrade A. was certainly angry, but it was clear he hadn't dared to talk to the journalist himself in this way, no doubt because he feared the man had friends in high places. Having unloaded his bitterness on me, however, Comrade A. then attended to my documents, and from that day on, I received my salary.

When a Party member goes abroad for a long time, he is supposed to turn in his Party membership card to the Central Committee of the C.P.S.U. The receipt he gets in exchange is to be presented to the appropriate Party organization abroad—at the embassy or trade mission or whatever.

In Peking, I had just as much trouble finding the assistant secretary of the Embassy's Party organization, Comrade O., as I had had finding other functionaries. While I tried to get in touch with him, he was evidently busy hearing the reports then circulating about certain events occurring in various places in China—whether true or false, I had never been able to ascertain.

Chinese "acts of aggression" against Soviet specialists and members of their families, the reports said, had occurred before, especially in 1957, but were becoming less frequent. There was a rumor that, in Manchuria, one Soviet specialist had been tossed out of a window but that the Chinese authorities had officially claimed the act a suicide. I also heard that somewhere in central China, near Sian, I believe, wives of Soviet specialists had been attacked at the market. There were other reports of that sort, including those stating that in certain districts, specialists who worked alone or in small groups had to live behind high walls and be guarded by special Chinese security troops.

In any case, after all the typical discussions and recommendations, Comrade O. eventually registered me as a Party member and assigned me to a small Party group of scientists, the secretary of which was U., a rather elderly geologist. We were all supposed "to raise our ideological and political level" by studying "selected problems of Marxist-Leninist philosophy." But we met only once a month—having all come to the same conclusion about the usefulness of our "ideological studies"— and followed the same rule I had adhered to myself during the twenty years I had been in charge of propaganda in such study groups, namely, to discuss only geography, history, biology, etc., and never touch on Marxism-Leninism except when a Party inspector joined us at the meetings (very rarely, thank goodness).

Nevertheless, a flare-up did occur once. During a discussion of the foundations of Marxist-Leninist dialectics, I expressed doubt that the same laws necessarily governed natural phenomena as governed society or human thought. "Where did they get these laws from?" I wanted to know. "Was it from experience, or were they derived from theory?"

The members of our group gaped at me in bewilderment. I was doing a shocking thing: I was questioning the validity of the basic premises of the Communist catechism! Several of my colleagues fell on me like unleashed dogs; I was battered on all sides with Marxist arguments. Now, I considered myself as well versed in Marxism-Leninism as any of them, but it was not a matter of knowledge or logic, but of faith—or, to be more exact, of conformity. Under Stalin, I would have been arrested for questioning this catechism; under Khrushchev, I would normally have been sharply reprimanded, branded an "idealist," and expelled from the Party. (Once, quite a few years ago, in the Soviet Union, I was severely taken to task during a seminar devoted to Engels' *Classification of Sciences* because I said that the purpose of this classification, as of any other, was above all determined by practical considerations and the convenience of its use. This was considered pure "pragmatism.") But the Soviet specialists in China were not a bloodthirsty lot, and the matter was tabled without even being mentioned in the report of the meeting.

CHAPTER FIVE

Drives and Campaigns

During the past twelve years, the Chinese rulers have tried to achieve some of their objectives by organizing crash campaigns involving either certain sections of the population or, sometimes, the entire nation. These campaigns, officially directed by the appropriate government agencies, are primarily supervised and spurred on by local Party organizations.

All these campaigns are given names, usually connoting the idea of combat or struggle, and are sometimes connected with certain numbers—the number of "enemies" to defeat or undesirable situations to eliminate. Thus, in 1952, the Chinese people were driven into the "Three-Anti" campaign against waste, corruption, and bureaucratic red tape; the following year, into the "Five-Anti" campaign against bribery, tax evasion, embezzlement of public property, fraud, and violation of state economic secrets.

Some campaigns are short and intensive, at least locally. For instance, the campaign to eliminate sparrows lasted for only three days in Peking. Other campaigns, however, such as the "Thought Reform Movement" or the "Great Leap Forward," may go on for years.

Some of these campaigns may seem simply ridiculous, even meaningless, but each of them brought suffering and degradation to millions of people, and many, such as the "Land Reform Movement" and the "Campaign to Suppress the Counterrevolutionary Movement," cost the lives of thousands and conceivably millions of people who were innocent even from a Communist point of view, let alone from a human one.

The measures taken during campaigns may at times be useful, as, for instance, those that improved sanitary conditions in the campaigns to exterminate flies and rats. But in such cases, a brief campaign is less effective than a permanent daily effort to control the pests: Although there were indeed very few flies in Peking in 1958, after the campaign, I found plenty of them in Kunming in 1960, when no one paid them special attention. In other instances, the campaigns took such absurd form that the direct results were—to use the dialectical jargon beloved by Marxists—the very antithesis of those sought, and the situation was made worse instead of better. In still other cases, the campaigns simply had no lasting effect on the people, access to the real information and genuine facts being enough to make all effects of the propaganda vanish. The Chinese attitude to the United States is a striking example of the inefficacy of the propaganda: Officially, the people "bellowed and roared" and had innumerable demonstrations against America; but I never met a single Chinese who privately expressed the slightest hostility to Americans.

The campaigns, in other words, did not affect the people deeply. The government nevertheless depended on them as a means to detect opponents to the regime and to influence the minds of the public. A Chinese, naturally undemonstrative and patient, tries to keep from being involved in anything that could make difficulties, so when the regime, striving to destroy this passivity, requires that he engage in these activities so contrary to his Chinese spirit, he simply *pretends* to do them.

The "Campaign against the Four Evils" began before my arrival in Peking. During my very first days in the city, my eye was caught by large posters with a picture of a woman in military uniform, a solemn and imperious lady pointing sternly at pictures of a rat, a sparrow, a fly, and a gnat—all four of which were crossed out with heavy red slashes, which meant that the government and Party were calling for their extermination.

One evening, walking in front of my hotel, I picked up a leaflet lying in the street. I was surprised to find it was written in Russian, and my surprise grew as I read it. It was addressed to the children of visiting Soviet experts, warning them not to interfere with the campaign against the sparrows that was to start in a few days, not to be afraid of shots, and, in general, to stay out of the way as much as possible.

Several days later, on Sunday, April 20, I was awakened in the early morning by a woman's bloodcurdling screams. Rushing to my window, I saw that a young woman was running to and fro on the roof of the building next door, frantically waving a bamboo pole with a large sheet tied to it. Suddenly, the woman stopped shouting, apparently to catch her breath, but a moment later, down below in the street, a drum started beating, and she resumed her frightful screams and the mad waving of her peculiar flag. This went on for several more minutes; then the drums stopped and the woman fell silent. I realized that in all the upper stories of the hotel, white-clad females were waving sheets and towels that were supposed to keep the sparrows from alighting on the building.

This was the opening of the anti-sparrow campaign. During the whole day, it was drums, gun shots, screams, and waving bedclothes, but at no time did I catch sight of a single sparrow. I cannot say whether the poor birds had sensed the deadly danger and taken off beforehand to some safer ground, or whether there had never been any sparrows in the first place. But the battle went on without abatement until noon, with all the manpower of the hotel mobilized and participating—bellboys, desk managers, interpreters, maids, and all.

The strategy behind this war on the sparrows boiled down to keeping the poor creatures from coming to rest on a roof or tree, thereby forcing them to remain constantly on the wing, for it was claimed that a sparrow kept in the air for more than four hours was bound to drop from exhaustion. And so, throughout the day and into the night, the drums continued to beat. Boys armed with little shotguns and slings rampaged over the city, aiming indiscriminately at any winged creature.

The results of this extermination drive were felt soon enough. The whole campaign had been initiated in the first place by some bigwig of the Party who had decided that the sparrows were devouring too large a part of the harvests. (It goes without saying that none of the qualified experts was consulted and that the whole campaign was conceived and planned by the Party, and executed under its supervision.) Soon enough, however, it was realized that although the sparrows did consume grain, they also destroyed many harmful insects which, left alive, inflicted far worse damage on the crops than did the birds. So the sparrows were rehabilitated. Rehabilitation, however, did not return them to life any more than it had the victims of Stalin's bloody purges, and the insects continued to feast on China's crops. Meanwhile, however, we Russians watched the slaughter of the sparrows with disgust, and those whose names were Vorobyov (which means "sparrow"), or Mukhin ("fly"), or Komarov ("gnat")—very common Russian names— gloomily joked about the mortal danger that threatened them.

Tatzepao, a "newspaper of large ideograms," is the Chinese equivalent of the "wall newspaper" that is found in every Soviet school, factory, or collective farm. These "newspapers" range from plain sheets of paper with pale, barely legible inscriptions found in the kolkhozes to huge colored posters illustrated with photographs, drawings, or cartoons in the universities at Moscow and Leningrad. These wall newspapers carry articles concerning certain matters to be studied or about production goals, political indoctrination, forthcoming holidays and anniversaries—all sorts of subjects. They may also contain some harmless criticisms of those "in charge." (At the high-water mark of Soviet "liberalism" in 1956, I saw in a wall newspaper at one major Soviet university an article in which it was openly stated that since the 1920's, Soviet literature had become nothing more than a cheap succession of hack-work writing, scorned by all and read by none.) In the Soviet Union, as a rule, wall newspapers appear no more than six times a year, preceding certain anniversaries and holidays, and once they are posted, they remain until the issuance of a new one.

In China, the wall press is somewhat different. I had noticed for some time the large sheets of colored paper covered with ideograms posted at the entrance to the Chemistry Institute, examples of the famous *tatzepao,* each usually consisting of two or three sheets. But imagine my amazement when, arriving one morning, I found every wall of the vestibule and corridor literally papered with these multicolored sheets. On the second day, the sea of paper had risen up the staircase, and, on the third day, it was all over the second floor. Apparently, the walls of every corridor were not sufficient to carry everything the Chinese wanted to say, for I found a line stretched down the middle of the hall with *tatzepao* hung from it like wash hung out to dry! They had evidently run out of colored paper, for these were made from old newspapers, with the thick black ideograms traced like insects over the print. As I was making my way through this paper jungle to my office, I saw Professor Liu reading a *tatzepao* hanging from the washline; there was a mournful expression on his face.

I became curious to learn what could have caused this sudden avalanche of *tatzepao*. My colleagues told me that the Party bosses had directed the administrators of every agency and institute to pay special attention to wall newspapers. Normally, each establishment is told by the Party organization in whose jurisdiction it is placed how many wall newspaper sheets it must issue and when. When a higher authority decides that wall newspapers should receive more emphasis, each local Party group competes in zeal and tries to outdo the others by driving the institutions it controls to put out more and more sheets, until the campaign takes on the proportions I have just described.

Of course, the time spent in producing *tatzepao* caused every Institute member to neglect his regular work for no less than two weeks. During this particular drive, each learned member was asked to put out ten sheets and each person employed on a menial job, five. But the Institute of Nonferrous Metals got away with less than four sheets per person. I was told that at the Ministry of Transportation, each employee produced 100 sheets on the average, and that, in Shanghai, a man claimed credit for 1,000 *tatzepao*.

What do the Chinese write in their wall newspapers? One Chinese girl, who was an interpreter for the visiting Russian specialist in organic chemistry, for instance, wrote about a colleague of hers who received a salary of 40 yüan, had her old mother to support, and nevertheless bought herself an expensive dress that cost 30 yüan. On the following day, the purchaser of the dress replied in her own *tatzepao*—which in China is as a rule written by one person, whether it consists of one sheet or several. This rebuttal sarcastically asserted that it ill befitted the accuser to speak of vanity, for she herself was the vainest girl in the Institute, the proof being the white ribbon she wore in her hair. Then the first girl explained in yet another *tatzepao* that her ribbon could hardly compare to the infamous dress, which cost about 100 times as much, the ribbon having cost only 35 fen. . . . This argument went on, I suppose, until each girl had filled her quota of *tatzepao* —in their case, five each.

Throughout my stay at the Institute, the announcements of my lectures were written in Chinese, but my name always figured in Russian letters. One morning, I noticed that my name appeared several times in a three-sheet *tatzepao*.

"What are they saying about me here?" I asked Li Fu-teh. "Do they write *tatzepao* about Soviet experts too? Do they criticize them?"

"No," he told me, "foreign specialists are not usually mentioned in the *tatzepao,* and if they are, it is always to say good things about them."

As about the dead, I thought, one never speaks ill of them. I inquired who had written it.

"Chou Liu-chi. She works under you, and she tells here how well you explain things and what a good worker you are."

"And you," I asked, "what did you write in your *tatzepao?*"

"Me? I don't belong to the scientific staff. I am classified as an employee of the administrative staff, so I only have to turn out five sheets."

"But what did you write about in those five sheets, since science is not your field?"

"It's true it's not my field, but I wrote one sheet about scientific work. I said that Professor Liu and the other leading scientists here were failing to make full use of Professor Klochko's services, that they forced him to postpone his lectures too often, and that they prevented members from attending many of his lectures by summoning them to meetings."

"But won't that get you into trouble?"

"It may, but I wrote what I believe to be true."

I remarked to my Chinese friends that I doubted the usefulness of all that gaudy display of paper, for each sheet, after being shown for a few days, yielded its place to a new one or was simply covered over. But my friends disagreed, assuring me that the interesting suggestions were noted down and used to remedy shortcomings and to further improvements. I inquired whether the girls' argument over the dresses and ribbons had been noted down, and was told not. My only conclusion could be that, whatever else, the time the girls had spent composing ten sheets of *tatzepao* had been completely wasted.

After several weeks, the flood of paper began to subside. The colored sheets disappeared first from the wash line, then from the corridor walls. After a few more days, only two or three blackboards remained where fanatics of denunciation and Party orthodoxy could continue their chalky exercises in prose, verse, and caricature.

Later, I found out who had initiated that idiotic campaign. By pure chance, I stumbled on a news item somewhere in the Russian-language *New China News Bulletin* or the magazine *Druzhba* reporting Mao's visit to a collective farm. In it, I read that,

> After he had greeted the officials and the workers, Chairman Mao walked over to the *tatzepao* and read it with great attention. He does this every time he visits an establishment or enterprise, because he considers the *tatzepao* very important.

I immediately saw the light: Mao thought *tatzepao* important and wished to see more of them! That was enough to trigger the campaign, and Party organizations from the Central Committee down to the local groups had set to, extracting *tatzepao* from everyone over whom they had power.

The constant effort made by the Party and the government to turn China's immense human resources into pliable material is periodically intensified to the point where it too becomes a farce. In March, 1958, such a spurt in the unceasing flood of propaganda was officially labelled the "Give One's Heart to the Party" campaign. As during the periodic "purges" in the Soviet Union, organizers of the campaign gathered together people working in the same departments, laboratories, institutes, etc., and set them at each other's throats. The selected victims were forced to make a clean breast of their sins—whether personal derelictions of duty or, even worse, some politically unorthodox pronouncement made by a distant relative—and, as they made these confessions, they were subjected to a barrage of questions from their colleagues, who seemed to feel their loyalty to the regime was in direct proportion to the venom they could pack into their queries.

But, whereas in the Soviet Union the matter of guilt and innocence was usually decided then and there on the spot, in China there were often several consecutive meetings to deal with a single victim. I know of a Chinese engineer who had to give his heart to the Party at thirteen meetings before it was accepted.

I realized that such a campaign was in progress in the Peking Institute during the spring of 1958, when the number of meetings increased until they were virtually continuous, so that it was difficult to find three consecutive free hours to lecture. Once, Su-fen told me she was afraid she might be criticized for having missed some unscheduled meeting or other while we were preparing a lecture.

"This afternoon," she said, "I should like, if I could, to take some time off, for I have other work to do." I let her go to her "other duties" and went over to the library. The reading room was quite empty. Usually, there were several dozen people working there, but now only the librarian and I. Everyone was at a meeting, I was told. At five-thirty, I returned to my office and found Su-fen writing at her little desk. I saw sheets of paper covered with her beautiful ideograms.

"What are you working on so hard?" I asked her.

"I am writing my confession. They will criticize me at the Party meeting tomorrow, and I will give my heart to the Party."

"Why, you are still so young! How can you possibly have had time to commit so many sins that one must hold a meeting to confess them?"

"I have been guilty of errors. I made statements that were wrong and harmful."

"What could you possibly have said?"

My last question seemed to embarrass Su-fen, and I did not insist on an answer. But later, when I was leaving for the hotel, she was still at work, telling of the evil deeds she had perpetrated against the Party and her people. What those could be was beyond me, for the girl was an ardent patriot, a loyal follower of Party instructions, as far as I knew, and a zealous worker.

After Su-fen had publicly confessed, I learned what it had been all about. She had expressed the profane thought that young Chinese should devote 80 per cent of their time to the building of socialism and 20 per cent to sports, reading, and relaxation. As they grew older, she said, they could devote more time to their duties, but while young, they should have time to train their bodies and minds for their future work. At the meeting, Su-fen confessed that she had been completely wrong and that she now realized that every citizen should devote nothing less than 100 per cent of his time to the building of Chinese socialism.

Su-fen was lucky, on the whole, for her recantation was accepted at that very meeting. Su Sao-bai, a young chemist and a very gifted woman, fared less well. It took a whole series of meetings to convince her accusers that she was sincerely sorry about a certain statement one of her relatives had made. (Obviously, while she was proving that her heart did belong to the Party, she had to suspend all her research completely.)

The Give One's Heart to the Party campaign spared no one. The most prominent scientists were liable to be "exposed" and subject to attacks from envious mediocrities. And the campaign was not all words. If the victim was deemed guilty, he might easily be packed off to "work on the land." In view of the fact that guilt could be established at will by the use of Communist casuistry, these hearings were supplemented with a sort of tariff levied on the Chinese scholarly establishments: Every member, every intellectual under fifty years of age, had to do a month of farm work each year, plus one whole year on the land in every five. The departure of these scientists to the country became a frequent sight in the streets of Peking, as they went off for remote provinces with their scanty belongings on their backs— a cleaning man, an engineer, and a professor, side by side. No one seemed to care about the abandoned research or the teacherless students. I suppose I should mention another curious consequence: According to a Chinese regulation, persons outside certain large urban centers are—heaven knows why—not allowed to maintain any correspondence with persons in foreign countries. One Chinese chemist was forced to interrupt a professional correspondence with a Soviet colleague while he was sent out of Peking for a year.

While taking a stroll along a broad avenue near the Summer Palace one day, I saw a pretty, small building and asked my Chinese companion what it was.

"That is one of the best maternity homes in Peking," I was told.

76

"And what do those four ideograms over the second-floor windows mean?"

"That is the latest Party slogan: 'More, better, faster, cheaper!' "

"Such a slogan on a maternity home? Is that the way the Party wants children to be produced?"

"No, but it applies to all aspects of economic and cultural development."

In 1958, of these four words, the emphasis was on the last, "cheaper." In the Institute, an exhibit devoted to economizing in materials and research apparatus was organized in a large room right across the hall from my office. It was called the "Anti-Waste Exhibit." There was an old book restored by a skilled bookbinder, and lab equipment made by Institute members from relatively simple parts; charts and diagrams showed which lab had unused equipment, how much it was worth, and the year of its purchase. For instance, one lab owned three similar pieces of apparatus of which only one was in use (although even that could hardly have been used much, since no work worth mentioning had been done in the labs for months). Other tables showed the labs' budgets, the number of research programs completed, etc.

Actually, there was nothing wrong with the idea of the exhibit, and some of the displays showed considerable ingenuity. But, looking at them all, I could not help but think that the whole concept was penny wise and pound foolish. The primary waste in the organization of Chinese science was in the wasted time of the people engaged in scientific work, rather than in any failure to utilize a piece of equipment or in carelessness with books. Beautiful, well-equipped labs stood deserted for days on end; thousands of technical books in excellent libraries remained closed while potential readers were at meetings, making confessions, or tilling the soil. This poor country, which had invested immense sums of hard currency between 1955 and 1958 to construct labs and libraries, had failed to use those capital investments. Trained personnel were distracted from their duties, and even the equipment was allowed to deteriorate through lack of proper maintenance.

I understand that there is a similar waste of manpower in Chinese factories. People are not taken away from their work quite so often, but three men will often do the work of one, although Soviet specialists told me this was done deliberately, to avoid unemployment.

CHAPTER SIX

A Trip South

Around the middle of March, my schedule provided for a trip to some of the southern provinces. I was to go to Shanghai, Nanking, and Hangchow to give a series of lectures and hold consultations with the staffs of various scientific institutions. Su-fen stayed behind in Peking, and in her place, a graduate student called Su Ke-ming was assigned to me as technical interpreter; Li Fu-teh also came along, of course, and it was understood that I and a Soviet specialist in organic chemistry would share his services in all day-to-day matters. He was also charged with the formalities of getting the train tickets, passes, etc.

Eventually all was ready, and at noon on the day of departure, we all met at the Peking railroad station. We easily gained entrance to the track platforms after showing to the armed sentries various gilt-edged documents provided by Li Fu-teh. Apparently these papers came from the Chinese security police and were in effect our passes for travel, a sort of visa required by white travelers.

The first thing we had to get used to on the train was the terrible racket: All day long, the loudspeaker emitted howls and wails accompanied by drumbeats, clashing cymbals, clanking irons, and a horrible squeaking and rattling. I was told, but could hardly believe, that the "music" was an excerpt from a Chinese opera. Whether it was or not, there was little we could do about it: It went on all day and one could not escape it. This was one of several occasions that convinced me that a Chinese reacts to noise differently from a European. Once, while I was talking with a visitor during office hours, Li Fu-teh started to talk with some young man who had dropped by in such loud tones that I could barely hear myself. I reprimanded him rather sternly, asking him whether it had occurred to him that his conversation was disturbing to me and to my visitor. He was genuinely surprised. "Why should it be?" he asked. "You don't understand Chinese."

As our trip wore on, the brown fields of the north were gradually replaced by vast stretches of bare black earth, then with green and densely planted fields. The landscape seemed strange and unfamiliar. In the Ukraine, where I had grown up, the fields are undulating and irregular, following the natural contours of the earth and throwing them into relief. Here, each field was flat and levelled; from afar, a series of them on a gentle incline looked like the steps of a low, wide staircase. Some of the steps were covered with water, but most of them were bare, yellow-gray patches marked off in narrow terraces. Li Fu-teh told me these were China's famous rice fields. Strangely enough, there was hardly a single human being to be seen working in them.

"But where are those five hundred million peasants?" my Soviet colleague wondered. "Why are they not in the fields? It's the spring planting season, isn't it?" The answer to that query could be found in the thousands of smoking chimneys we saw each day, and in the fires that were visible every night over half the horizon. The peasants were carrying out the orders of the Party, working night and day at the mines and at home-made blast furnaces to fulfill the "Drive to Produce Metals Locally." And we know the results: They did not obtain any more iron than before, and there was much less bread and rice to go around.

This much talked-about drive was only one of many efforts to organize small local centers of industrial production. Now, coal extracted from small local mines can perhaps be used in a kitchen stove, but the extraction and manufacture of cast iron or steel is a much more complex venture than cooking a meal. According to the official figure, 4 million tons of iron were processed in small local furnaces, but of this amount, hardly more than 1 per cent was usable, the remaining 99 per cent being slag, unwashed ore, or even more often, a pure invention of the statisticians.

One day, *Jen Min Jih Pao* announced that some Chinese chemist had proposed a new method of obtaining aluminum by using sodium in the form of metal. There was actually nothing new about the method, for eighty years ago, it was widely used. But only since the method was replaced by electrolysis of fused cryolite (a sodium-aluminum fluoride)—a molten mass into which aluminum oxide obtained from bauxite is dissolved—did aluminum become easily and cheaply available. Nowadays, sodium is no cheaper than aluminum, and being highly inflammable, it presents a fire hazard when not handled with special precautions. The obvious question is whether it is simpler to obtain aluminum by the cryolite electrolysis method at large plants or by the "new" method, for which one must first obtain sodium and then send it out into the villages—the transportation of sodium being in itself an extremely expensive matter. The answer seems clear, yet, so far as I know, no Chinese chemist raised his voice in protest against *Jen Min Jih Pao*'s idiotic suggestion.

At first sight, another proposal I came across for the local processing of copper made more sense, because that metal has been produced in small furnaces in China for generations, and the people have considerable experience in the process. But the main objection is that when copper is obtained from sulfide ores, there may also be gold and silver in quantities sufficient to make it economically expedient to use the electrolysis method, which would yield the precious metals as by-products. Just before I left China in 1958, I pointed out the impracticality of local methods of copper processing, which lose the precious metals and which also fail to extract the full measure of the metal from the ore.

On the morning of the third day of our trip, we traversed a wide plain crisscrossed by hundreds of canals; on some of them, there were little sailboats. The planted fields had become positively luxuriant, but soon gave way to villages, towns, and eventually, the interminable suburbs of China's largest city. We had arrived in Shanghai.

A welcoming committee from the local branch of the Academy of Sciences greeted us at the railroad station and then took us to the famous hotel Astor House, an "old world" establishment in the heart of the European sector of Shanghai, where even the bellboys wore European suits and spoke English.

Our first business was, of course, to visit Futan University and the institutes. The university, housed in large and spacious buildings, occupies a fairly extensive section of suburban Shanghai. The chemistry department building was being completed while I was there, and opposite it, a large university library was under construction. Although the auditorium was completely filled for my lecture, I never saw any students in the labs, for they were all at meetings. But I was kept busy discussing the programs the university had planned for laboratory work in physical chemistry, and giving consultations on what were actually rather interesting and useful research projects. (In one lab, a Russian scientist,

P. S. Bogoyavlensky, was working with several assistants on the solutions of different salts in water.)

The Shanghai normal school, in some contrast to the unfinished university, was strikingly beautiful. Its white buildings and green lawns surrounded by canals, the flowerbeds and trees, the space and light were not unlike an Oriental version of Cambridge. On the other hand, the Polytechnical Institute presented a different picture. Its huge, unattractive buildings, in China's dreary box-like style of modern architecture, were scattered at random over a large area that was still torn up and defaced by construction work. The administrator of the Institute told me that when the construction was finished, the Institute would be larger than any other, an achievement that appeared to excuse all.

But what interested me most in all of Shanghai was my visit to one of China's oldest research institutes, the Institute for Research in Metallurgy and Ceramics. I was received there by the famous Chou Jen, a great scholar and scientist whose personal charm was magnetic and immediately appealing. As head of ceramics production there, he had spent forty years of his life studying the composition of Chinese porcelain and the methods of producing it. The production of fine porcelain is an extraordinarily complex process, in which the two components—kaolin and feldspar—must be mixed in careful proportion, and in which the firing and baking of the material must be accomplished with the most precise timing and at scrupulously maintained temperatures. Porcelain, like many other substances, undergoes in the course of firing a series of subtle transformations; it is very important that they take place according to a flawless, controlled cycle. It is for this reason that the manufacture of porcelain is a veritable art. I gathered from our conversation that, despite his years of studying different methods, Chou Jen was far from possessing all the secrets of the master porcelain makers of old China, whose works are such a remarkable testimony to their technical abilities and artistic taste.

Professor Chou Jen showed me his labs, his collection of micro-photographs of all kinds of porcelain, and, finally, his collection of antique Chinese porcelain, a beautiful array that is probably unique in the world. Some of the pieces were centuries old, but their colors and condition were as dazzling and beautiful as if they had only just been taken from the kiln. I incidentally learned that the famous celestial blue of old Chinese porcelain came from cobalt ores mined in Katanga. Five or six hundred years ago, Chinese sailors went regularly to the east coast of Africa to get cobalt brought from Katanga for the master porcelain makers.

The other labs at the Institute and the staff itself I also found quite impressive. The senior members were in no way less qualified than their opposite numbers at the Institute of Metallurgy in the Soviet Union, but there were fewer of them. Work was done there on refractory materials that are extremely important in metals production, and also on the properties of various alloys.

The Shanghai nonferrous metals factory, which I saw a few days later, is a complex of buildings between which are yards cluttered with heaps of copper scraps and wire, old kettles, coins, boilers, and metal household items. (I imagine that many of these objects, especially the coins, were valuable and interesting enough to be worthy of a place in a Western museum.) One of the buildings contained the foundry, and I visited there first. What most appalled me about the foundry was the incredible racket coming from loudspeakers, which were relaying some radio program or other, the noise rising high above the whistling steam, the hissing molten metal, and the clang of crucibles. I pointed out to my guides that such a deafening noise was truly inadmissible in a foundry, where the workers had to operate at a pitch of high concentration at every moment, since any careless movement could cause the most horrible burns, maiming, or death. But my hosts only smiled sweetly. The Chinese are so accustomed to noise that even in a dangerous place like a foundry, they keep stuffing propaganda down the workers' throats, without it ever occurring to them that they may thereby endanger lives.

From conversations I had with the plant's engineers, I came to the conclusion that the factory was nevertheless blessed with a staff well trained in the technology of nonferrous and precious metals, and that the reputation Shanghai metallurgists enjoy for their intelligence, resourcefulness, and the high quality of their work is well justified. (The electrolysis shop was particularly well organized at that plant.) In this respect, Shanghai can very well be compared to Leningrad, whose engineers, technicians, and workers are the most highly qualified in the Soviet Union.

Besides my various consultations in Shanghai, I also gave two lectures to packed audiences, with a crowd of the curious pressing around the windows outside. Apparently they only rarely had a chance to see and hear someone who was not Chinese.

Almost every Soviet specialist who goes to China visits Hangchow, the principal city of the maritime province of Chekiang, about 110 miles southwest of Shanghai. An ancient Chinese saying remarks that "Heaven has its Paradise and Earth has its Hangchow and Soochow." And so, I visited both these paradisaic cities.

The trip from Shanghai to Hangchow is an enchanting one. The train rolls through a beautifully cultivated countryside; it was spring when I went, and everything was flourishing and in bloom. The young emerald-green rice shoots reflected in the water, the yellow flowers growing along the roads, the little tea plants on the gentle slopes—they all seemed to belong to a magical kind of landscape, bathed in the soft light of the declining sun.

When we arrived at Hangchow, I was met by a Professor Chin, whom I had heard about in the Soviet Union, where his papers on solutions appeared in the Soviet *Journal of Physical Chemistry*. The next day, I went with him to the normal school, installed in the rather elegant brick buildings of a former American college. It was evident there that the *tatzepao* campaign had arrived in Hangchow: Just as in the Peking Institute, the walls were covered with posters; along the halls and even in the courtyards, they were strung out and pasted in every possible place.

My talks with Professor Chin and his colleagues persuaded me of their great understanding of many problems in theoretical chemistry and the creativity and imaginativeness of their approach to scientific work. But perhaps the most interesting scientist I met in Hangchow was an old professor engaged in an analysis of various antique metal objects—pots and pans, tools, and coins. This is fascinating research, yielding valuable information for a historian as well as for a technologist or chemist, for it reveals not only the age of the artifact, but the precise components of the materials used in its production. He showed me, for instance, seven-hundred-year-old copper coins, which he had discovered to contain nickel, a metal that was not discovered in the West until the eighteenth century. His research had demonstrated that there is good reason to believe that certain Central Asian coins were minted from Chinese alloys of copper and nickel as early as the first centuries A.D.

Once my lectures and consultations were over, I spent my leisure time in visiting the city. Hangchow is built along the edge of West Lake, the focal point of the city's magnificent natural site. Apparently, this lake was once an arm of the sea, from which it was gradually separated by alluvial deposits, becoming a fresh-water lake as a result of the river water that pours into it from several small sources. The lake is split into three parts by two dams, along the crests of which are beautiful woods with paths for walking. The shores of the lake are wooded too, and, together with the miniature green islands with their shady arbors and little temples, form a really enchanting picture.

I should have liked to have stayed and enjoyed the delights of Hangchow longer, but soon I had to return to Shanghai. En route from there to Nanking, however, I made a detour to Soochow, a city of marvels, famous for its palaces (more than 100) with their antiques, vases, and paintings. These palaces are for the most part rather small houses of only eight or ten rooms, but very handsomely and elegantly constructed. At first, it may seem that all the art treasures have been placed there in complete disorder, but in truth they are arranged with consummate taste, leaving one with the over-all impression, as one goes from one to another, of visiting a beautiful, city-wide museum of Chinese antique art. In the old days, the inhabitants of these colorful palaces lived in complete isolation from the bustle of the outside world, but now the buildings are owned by the state and are open to the public.

The people who live in Soochow evidently see foreigners very rarely, for our appearance excited the most lively curiosity and interest. On our way to visit Soochow's department store, we were surrounded at all points by a huge crowd of staring children, and, when I waited outside the store for my colleagues to make some purchases, I gradually realized that a human ring was forming around me, consisting of both children and adults who were staring at me quite unabashedly. The ring began to tighten, so I opened our car door and got inside. Now, at least, I thought, the people would go away and leave me in peace. But they had no thought of leaving! Faces were glued to all the windows of the car and the windshield as well; for another half-hour, I sat as in a veritable fish-bowl before being rescued by my friends.

Nanking—whose name means "southern capital" as Peking means "northern capital"—where we arrived after our visit in Soochow, is one of the most interesting of all Chinese cities. We arrived at night and were met at the station, with the customary Chinese hospitality and courtesy, by Professor Tai, dean of the chemistry faculty of Nanking University, and Professor Kuo, a specialist in organic chemistry and deputy president of the university. Both these men were distinguished scientists; under the pressure of political instructions from above, however, their researches gave way to more "practical" work.

Like Peking University, Nanking University has twelve departments: in mathematics, physics, chemistry, geology, history, Chinese language and literature, etc., but I and my Soviet colleague in organic chemistry visited only those departments in our own fields.

The university has wonderfully spacious labs, both for its students and for research; the physical chemistry lab in particular was stunning—a place that could accommodate 200 people working at once. But there were no students in the deserted labs.

I gave my two lectures at the local branch of the Chinese Academy of Sciences, in a beautiful building in the old Chinese style with a green tile roof, located at the edge of the city in a virtually rural district near the Temple of the Rooster. My interpreter must have been in great form, for his translation was obviously much more expressive and eloquent than what I had said myself. I saw that the audience, especially the women, watched him with an enthusiasm that was not quite accounted for by the subject of my lecture, and I was impressed by their applause. But Su Keming was, indeed—with his inspired voice, his shining eyes, and his tall, erect figure—the personification of a young scientist brimming over with enthusiasm for the learning and the calling to which he had devoted his life.

Unlike Peking, where there were so many new buildings going up, Nanking had few new houses. New buildings or not, I could not understand why the Chinese had chosen Peking rather than Nanking as their capital. Peking is located in the outer perimeter of the country, while Nanking is close to the central, populous parts of China in which about 80 per cent of the Chinese population is concentrated. (Peking was the capital of China for the 400 years during which the country was ruled by foreign dynasties. Before that, for several centuries, Nanking had been the capital, and it was made so once again by the Kuomintang in the 1930's.)

The countryside around Nanking is charming and picturesque, and I luckily had the opportunity to enjoy it when I went to visit the Tzu Chin Shan Observatory, perched on the top of a hill outside the city. The Observatory has a famous collection of old astronomical instruments, remarkable for their continuing precision and the ingenuity of their design. One antique instrument for determining the position of the heavenly bodies, placed quite unprotected under the open sky, not far from the Observatory, stands on legs of polished and beautifully carved metal shaped like dragons. I was told that in all of China, only two of these incredible instruments existed; both had been taken away by Western powers; one had now been returned, but its twin was still, we were told, in West Germany. A woman who worked in the Observatory and who showed us around enumerated a number of other objects of great historic and artistic value which had been removed by foreigners and had not been returned to the Chinese people. This looting—for that is actually what it should be called—began, she told us, around the middle of the nineteenth century and went on well into the twentieth. To this very day, many of China's cultural relics are in foreign museums.

I learned in Nanking that there used to be people in old China whose particular occupation it was to find appropriate burial spots for rich or important personages. Apparently, a whole team of such professional searchers was engaged to find a worthy resting place for the great Chinese statesman Sun Yat-sen. And so, today, a sober and beautiful mausoleum stands on the slope of a green hill just outside Nanking—a building of modest but harmonious proportions which one approaches from a flight of wide stairs leading up a bank of terraces. Inside, from the central domed hall, a stairway leads down to a dimly lighted room in which Sun Yat-sen's coffin is laid. As I left this beautiful and impressive spot, I could not help but compare it with the ugly and inartistic block of stones that is Lenin's resting place in Red Square. But my good impression of the Chinese monument was spoiled by the sight of uniformed soldiers playing cards in the shadow of the building.

CHAPTER SEVEN

A Trip North

Three months after my trip to the southern provinces of China, in June, 1958, I visited several cities in northeast China and Manchuria—Mukden (Shenyang), Changchun, Tientsin, and others, this time accompanied by Su-fen and Su Sao-bai. Various members of local enterprises in Mukden who had consulted me in Peking had asked me to go there, so that was my first stop.

Mukden is the industrial center of Manchuria, the center of the metallurgical industries and possibly the second most important industrial city in China after Shanghai. The nonferrous metals works there is one of the oldest industrial plants in the country, a plant whose main product is copper but which also produces other nonferrous metals. Arriving in the courtyard of the factory, I suddenly realized that before my eyes lay a microcosmic display of the entire history of transportation from the Stone Age to the mid-twentieth century. Loads were being moved about on men's backs, on donkeys, on horses, in carts, and in the most ultra-modern trucks. In the shadow of brand-new and beautifully equipped buildings, antediluvian tools and instruments were still employed in archaic shops.

The mess in the courtyard, with its heaps of scrap metal and sloppy streamlets of copper and nickel sulfate solutions running between, was mirrored by the chaos within the buildings, especially in the shops where precious metals—gold and silver primarily—were processed from the residues obtained in the electrolytic purification of copper. Thick smoke poured out of the kilns, carrying off particles of the precious metals; the tanks where the pure silver was deposited were in no better shape. The entire establishment quite shocked me, especially in comparison with the Shanghai plant I had visited, where at least in some shops one found relative order and efficiency.

The day after this visit, a conference was held at the plant on the various metallurgical problems at the factory, and I was asked my impressions of the enterprise. I decided to discard politeness and told them how shocked I was, when I considered China's shortage of nonferrous and, above all, precious metals, to find such wastefulness and inefficiency at a major plant. I specified the particular instances that caused the wastage, recommending to the management that the sections where gold and silver were refined be closed down forthwith. My hosts were shocked and taken aback by my outburst, but they asked me to discuss with them the measures needed to eliminate the shortcomings I had pointed out and promised to do their best to remedy the situation. I must do them justice: They kept their word. When I visited the plant two years later, in 1960, it was in much better order, especially the two shops I had criticized most.

We visited two other plants near Mukden, one a large aluminum plant built by Soviet engineers and modelled on the Zaporozhe plant on the Dnieper; it was operating at only two-thirds capacity. Nevertheless, they were trying to organize the production of light metals—sodium, calcium, and lithium—obtained, like aluminum, by the electrolysis of molten salts.

The other plant produced chemical fertilizers, particularly ammonium nitrates. Because of the importance of fertilizers to China's pressing agricultural problems, I was especially interested in this plant. Several centuries ago, Chinese agriculture had been the most advanced in the world: The methods of planting—each rice shoot being planted separately, as is done for cabbages or tomatoes—the intelligently constructed irrigation systems, the hothouses, and the intensive use of fecal matter for fertilizer had made tremendous yields possible. But these agricultural triumphs were dwarfed by the sharp increase in the past 150 years in the yield of grain crops in the West, an increase due to the introduction of the latest scientific findings and, above all, to the use of chemical fertilizers. Who would have imagined that millions of tons of ammonia gas, that substance once known only for its unpleasant smell of decaying urine, would be produced each year, and that on the immense scope of its production would depend the nourishment of hundreds of millions of people.

As I investigated the fertilizer plant's equipment, I warned my hosts against the use of iron or steel spades or shovels when working with ammonium nitrates, since the contact with the metal causes the latter rapidly to decompose, and the resulting gases take up a space hundreds of times as great as the nitrate in its solid state. In Germany, in the 1920's, a terrible explosion which cost hundreds of lives was caused by digging with an iron pick in a nitrate heap.

Still, the plant impressed me as one capable of producing a significant amount of fertilizers and methyl alcohol, though during our visit, the latter was not being manufactured for lack of demand for it. I wondered, as we made our tour, how many such factories would have to be built before China's people would be adequately fed. So far, there were only an isolated few, and this despite the fact that there is no country in the world (with the possible exception of India) whose future welfare is so closely bound to the development of chemical fertilizers. But the rulers of China today do not seem to realize this, and for the past twelve years, they have concentrated their efforts on everything else (especially military preparations) to the detriment of the country's agricultural development. All the while, the population has been increasing at a tremendous rate, and the feeble attempts made to arrest the population growth between 1956 and 1958 have been discarded. There was a serious food shortage during the second half of 1958 (the year of the "record harvest"), and the shortage still exists, as can be clearly gauged from China's purchases of grain abroad.

Changchun, the capital of Kirin Province and the former capital of the wartime Japanese puppet state Manchukuo, had a research institute engaged in the study of certain chemical problems. After 1949, it was named the Institute of Applied Chemistry and was considered, along with the Peking Chemistry Institute, the most important center of chemical research in the Chinese Academy of Sciences.

In the summer of 1958, China's scientific institutions were going through one of those revision campaigns which usually last for two or three months and during which the scientists spend all their time discussing the programs instead of trying to carry them out. During this campaign, it was decided to send a group of Peking's leading chemists to Changchun to work out a coordinated program for both establishments. This happened to coincide with my trip to that city, and so I joined a group of more than twenty members of the Peking Research Institute.

Li Fu-teh, who had accompanied me on my spring tour to southern China, stayed behind in Peking, so Chou Su-fen combined her regular job as my scientific translator with the function of personal interpreter and guide. The diminutive young girl impressed everyone with her seriousness and dignity, and that was why she was allowed to join Professor Liu and me, on the trip to Changchun, in a compartment with *upholstered* seats!—a rare luxury in China—while all the learned chemists traveled on wooden benches.

At Changchun, we were met by a delegation from the Institute headed by the director, Professor Wu Hseueh-chou. This elegant, affable man had, in his youth, worked in the United States on the optics of solutions, whence he had managed to bring back not only some scientific experience, but a lot of research apparatus that one could obtain there. Now, the instruments lay idle in the Institute's darkroom, respectfully draped with black covers and a thick layer of dust, while Professor Wu, conforming to the directives of the Party, turned from a research scientist into an administrator, constantly repeating the modern slogan that politics had priority over science. No doubt, he was not anxious to repeat the experiences of his predecessor, who, not fully grasping the puzzling truth of that slogan, had continually pointed out that the endless political meetings and conferences were consuming huge quantities of the scientists' time, and that there was no time left for research. Such a failure to grasp the true role of science in the Chinese Communist state could not go unpunished: The director was "exposed" as a "right-wing deviationist," removed from his post, and sent to some remote district to "work on the land" and to absorb the wisdom of the masses. Professor Wu was appointed in his place, a more flexible man who understood immediately what the mighty ones desired. He was rewarded by various advancements in his social, economic, and material status, and his two daughters were allowed to take piano lessons—a truly staggering privilege in Red China.

Among the other people who came to meet us was one Professor Pang. One of the homonyms of his name means "fat," but this man was strikingly thin, and his thinness was accentuated by his unusual height. I had met him in Peking: He was a great specialist on rare elements, and spoke some Russian and English.

The Institute of Applied Chemistry is situated in a wooded area just beyond Changchun—a complex of administrative and laboratory buildings of differing ages. The workshops and laboratories were well equipped, and the Institute even had its own foundry and a glass-blowing shop, also a radio shop. (We did not have a foundry in our Moscow Institute.) After spending two weeks there, I was convinced that not only did it have adequate facilities and an excellent large library, but that there were some good scientists on its staff. In brief, it had everything but one crucial element—there was no time for work. The researchers' days were mercilessly torn apart and wasted on countless meetings, and what time they had left for scientific work was spent mostly on revision of their programs.

During the last few days I was there, I had the doubtful pleasure of attending the meetings devoted to revision of the Changchun Institute's work program—the third revision, I was given to understand, undertaken that year. Everything done up to that point was discarded, *tout court*, without bothering to find out how much time it would take to complete it or to discuss whether the work was in fact useful or necessary. Naturally, the new plans were in no way better than the discarded ones, and often worse. The scientists' opinions were never the deciding factor and often were not taken into consideration at all. It was not surprising that the new plans were drafted without any thought as to the material possibilities or the availability of qualified personnel. The tune was called by ignorant Party officials and executed by the even more ignorant members of the local Party agencies—people who, as a rule, deeply distrust scientists, whom they consider to be representatives of bourgeois ideology and full of "class hostility" for the proletariat.

It was no wonder, since logical arguments could have had little effect on these Party vigilantes, that the scientists, familiar as they were with campaigns against "right-wing elements," submitted passively and allowed themselves to be driven by the winds of Party propaganda. One could, perhaps, explain the behavior of some of them by fear and indifference—fear of displeasing the mighty, and indifference to everything in the world except their personal survival and the safety of their families. But they could hardly have changed the attitude of the Party men toward science in any case.

The new programs devised at these conferences were scrapped, just like all the preceding ones; only six weeks later, they were pronounced "impractical," as Hua Shao-chun told me a few days before I left China.

Later on during my stay in Changchun, I paid a visit to the university. The department of chemistry there was working on the problem of obtaining germanium from coal ash. In recent years, germanium has been used as a material for semi-conductors (and as such is important in radio-electronics), and there seems to be a possibility of finding it in coal ash in the necessary industrial quantities. I saw very few students in the university laboratories, but this could be accounted for by the fact that it was summer and they may have been working in factories.

Like every foreign visitor in Changchun, I was also offered a visit to an automotive plant, built by Russian engineers, that produced trucks. A group of us visited the factory together with a group of Buddhist monks. Judging by the conveyor belt, the plant seemed to be working rather slowly and, although it was fairly new, neither the yards nor the shops were in good order. I did not know what the gasoline situation was in China; I simply assumed that most of China's petroleum and petroleum products came from the Soviet Union. But if China is to develop its industry and agriculture to any appreciable degree, she would need scores of factories like this one.

Changchun is a green city—the very name means "eternal spring"—and its straight, broad avenues are lined with trees. While I was there, the weather was extremely pleasant; it was not too hot, and the gardens and parks looked particularly luxuriant. One afternoon, during a walk, we saw a parade going from the old quarters of the city to the new. A tall, thin fellow, his face covered with red paint and a top hat on his head, walked at the head of the procession—he was supposed to represent "Eisenhower, the chief of the American imperialists." There followed a whole regiment of boys and girls in columns of four, wearing all sorts of different attire, most of them with their cheeks smeared with red and pink paint. As soon as Su-fen and I appeared, the crowd of children that had been following the parade abandoned it and latched on to us.

It began to grow dark, lanterns appeared; a few boys began to dance to the accompaniment of drums; the children were crowding close around us. I made the mistake of starting to play with some of them—and it was a long time before we could make our escape back to the hotel.

Professor Liu and I did not return to Peking directly, but turned instead to Dairen, Port Arthur, and also the salt marshes of the Liaotung Peninsula, for we took advantage of our stay in Dairen to go to see the salt marshes along the north coast of the Gulf of Po Hai. One reaches them by going along a beautiful road that winds along the edge of the sea. Viewed from afar, the dyke-bound salt marshes looked like huge framed mirrors reflecting the sky and clouds, their color varying from dark blue to the palest green tinged with yellow. These salt marshes are not far from Fuhsien, a town which, like Dairen, Port Arthur, and other towns of the Liaotung Peninsula, suffers from a shortage of fresh water. This shortage could be alleviated if a project for the desalinization of (and reclamation of land from) the Gulf of Po Hai—a project I outlined at some length during my stay in China —were carried out.

A glance at the map of China shows us that the Gulf of Po Hai offers exceptional opportunities for desalinizing some of its waters, draining other areas covered by it, and using the land for agriculture. It is the point where the ocean makes its deepest penetration into continental China, bringing the seaports along it close to the inland cities; the gulf itself is relatively shallow (meaning that the volume of water is not great in relation to the surface, so that one could evaporate or desalinize it quite rapidly); it has a large river flowing into it; its connection with the sea is only a strait that is very narrow in comparison with the length of the shores of the gulf; and the climate of the region is excellent, with adequate precipitation.

I calculated that, according to the amount of fresh water now emptying into the Gulf of Po Hai and the amount of salt water that could be released over a dam built across the strait, the salt content of the Gulf's waters could be reduced to 0.3 per cent in thirty-six years, a level at which the water would be suitable for irrigation and other purposes. It would also be possible to drain part of the gulf once this were accomplished. I developed these ideas in detail in a paper that I gave to the directors of the Peking Institute before I left China, and it was later published in the Chinese Chemical Journal. I realized that vast and comprehensive research was needed to carry out such an ambitious plan, but I expressed my faith that it was entirely possible.

CHAPTER EIGHT

My Last Weeks in Peking:
We Talk Politics

After I returned from the north, I resumed my work at the Peking Institute—completing my lecture course, giving more consultations, and helping the members of the Institute in their research.

On July 10, my six-month visit to China was to end. But Professor Liu, I later learned, pleaded with the Embassy to have my stay prolonged, and, since the Moscow authorities did not object, I stayed for an additional six weeks, leaving China only on August 22.

On August 1, I bid good-by to Professor Liu and Professor Lepeshkov, who were leaving for Tsinghai on an expedition to the salt marshes. (While in Peking, Lepeshkov had been in charge of the study of salts, leaving me to devote my time to writing a paper on the utilization of the Gulf of Po Hai and to organizing research in mineral chemistry and the study of precious metals.)

When Liu and Lepeshkov left for Tsinghai, and many of the students had gone to work in the villages, the Institute seemed deserted. Attempts were even made to send Su-fen to work in the country, but I insisted that it would be extremely difficult to go on holding consultations without her assistance.

One of her last services to me was to act as interpreter during my political discussions with Hua Shao-chun, the deputy director of the Institute in charge of Party affairs.

Hua Shao-chun—whose name means "flower"—was a very colorful personality. Even as I write these lines, I can see that slender figure, with his proletarian airs, his cloth cap pulled low down on his forehead. (Unlike most other Chinese, who liked to go bareheaded even in the street, Hua Shao-chun kept his hat on indoors.)

At that time, he had been a Party member for more than twenty years; he was a veteran of the Chinese civil war and, I believe, of the Long March. (Since many of his former comrades-in-arms occupied positions in other institutes equivalent to his, his assistance was most useful.) There was nothing particularly imposing in the man's physical appearance, but his eyes were unforgettable, burning with a flame of suspicion and hatred of the people who, in his opinion, uselessly cluttered Chinese soil. Among such creatures, he classified all scientists without distinction; they were class enemies of the workers and peasants and therefore his personal enemies too.

When I was about to leave for Tientsin to expound my ideas on the utilization of the Gulf of Po Hai, Hua Shao-chun said to me, "Don't go to the scientists with your idea. Don't expect any assistance from them. Nothing will come of it. Go directly to the city Party committee instead. They will help you in what you are trying to do."

Twice during the summer of 1958, Hua and I had conversations on political subjects. These conversations would take place in my office, where he would install himself on the small sofa facing my desk, cross his legs, and, fixing his gaze on some invisible object on the corner of my desk, begin to speak in a voice so low that Su-fen had to lean toward him to hear what he was saying. Gradually, his voice would rise, although he continued to speak very slowly and with many pauses.

"It so happens," he began once, in a roundabout way, "that we are interested in melting the snow and glaciers in certain districts of our country. In the spring, when our fields need water so badly, the melting doesn't start soon enough, while in the summer, when the melting reaches its highest point, the water flows away uselessly."

I told him I had never made a special study of that problem, but I suggested that it would be worthwhile trying to cover the ice and snow with some black substance like coal dust; the sun's rays, instead of being reflected from the white surface, would be absorbed, and the melting process would be speeded up.

But I realized that snow-melting was only a topic he had raised to give himself a chance to warm up. Changing the subject abruptly, he opened up a direct attack on our Institute and its entire membership. "The best thing," he declared, "would be to put a padlock on the door and chase all the members away." I gaped at him in bewilderment. "I mean it," he went on. "While the other institutes do accomplish something, even if very little, for the national economy, our Institute is of no use whatsoever."

No longer able to restrain myself, I told him what I thought of the matter myself and cited the opinion of some of the other Soviet specialists in China. I assured him that, by and large, we all shared the same opinion as to the causes of Chinese backwardness in science. I am sure that Su-fen somewhat softened the tone of what I said, but, even in this diluted form, it seemed to give him a shock. I actually tried to make two points: first, that scientific research, like any other job, required time to show results, and that Chinese scientists were deprived of that indispensable commodity by the political meetings at which their attendance was required. The better Soviet experts were anxious to help in China's scientific development, and they were irritated when their Chinese colleagues were forced to spend more time at useless meetings than working at their research. I told Hua what the consensus of opinion was among many of the Soviet specialists: "The Chinese can catch up with us and overtake us as soon as they start working in their characteristic Chinese style, and give up those idiotic conferences." As it was, Chinese scientists were forced to waste not only their own time but also the Soviet advisers' and the money paid them by the Chinese government.

The second element retarding the progress of Chinese science was the leadership's distrust of their scientists. For what else did those endless changes in the research programs signify? As soon as a scientist began research on a given topic after spending several months in preparations and in collecting apparatus, he was almost always told to abandon his work, that what he was attempting would be of no use to the national economy, that it would not contribute to the building of socialism in China, and that he had better switch to something else, something that in the Party's opinion was more urgent. The scientists had no choice but to obey. They would prepare themselves anew for different research, and the same thing would happen all over again. There could be only one possible explanation for this state of affairs— distrust of the scientists' good sense and patriotic sincerity. "For example," I said to Hua, "did not you recommend that I not entrust my Po Hai project in Tientsin to the scientists there?"

Hua looked surprised at my aggressiveness. He began to argue that the propaganda of the Party line was a very important thing, very necessary.

"In 1957," he said, "the situation in China was close to what it was in Hungary in 1956. And many of our intellectuals had right-wing views. Besides," he went on, "many subjects of research are impractical and useless."

I did not agree, and replied that I considered the work done on salts and polymeric compounds, for instance, of great practical importance. There were other industrial fields in which research was greatly needed, but still, I insisted, in order to make progress in any field of chemical technology, a great deal of time had to be devoted to pure science, to basic research. Without it, Chinese science would never be able to stand on its own feet and would be doomed to imitation and to picking up other peoples' ideas. No matter how hard I tried, I think I never succeeded in making Hua understand this last point.

Hua and I remained good friends despite the sharpness of my remarks—at least, I noticed no evidence of malice in his attitude. Our last conversation took place two days before my departure. He told me then that my Chinese colleagues' devotion of time to so many political meetings was only a temporary measure. Yet the "temporary measure" continued from late 1957 until 1960, and as far as I know, was still going on in 1961, although on a somewhat reduced scale.

Besides their concern with the indoctrination of their own cadres, China's rulers tried to spread their political views to other countries. The instruments by means of which Party propaganda was spread were foreign-language broadcasts, books, pamphlets, and magazines. Among the English-language magazines published in Peking, I remember particularly the *Peking Review* and *China Reconstructs*. A special publishing house for foreign-language books produced books mostly in English, and Russian books or journals were relatively scarce, although all the speeches of Mao, Chou En-lai, and other statesmen were translated. There was, however, a Russian-language *New China News Bulletin,* a four- or eight- or ten-page publication issued by the New China News Agency.

In 1958, the Chinese did not try openly to subvert the visiting Soviet advisers or even to present viewpoints that would obviously clash with official Soviet policy. The Russian-language broadcasts and the *New China News Bulletin* were officially sanctioned among the Soviet specialists, although echoes of disagreements began to be heard after Khrushchev's visit to Peking from July 31 to August 2, 1958. (Actually, we only learned of that visit because air communications between Moscow and Peking were interrupted for those three days and travel by Soviet technicians and scientists in either direction was delayed.) Things were very different in 1960. Then, Chinese authorities openly proposed to us opinions that were pure heresy from the Soviet viewpoint.

Chinese views on international policy, as they were expressed in Chinese and foreign-language journals, were not too complicated. There were two implacable enemies of the socialist countries and the workers of the world: "American Imperialism" and "Yugoslav Revisionism." Compared with these two plagues, all the other "imperialisms" were unworthy of being taken seriously. In 1958, the first of the two great enemies were symbolized by President Eisenhower, and the second by President Tito. Tito probably received even more attention and invective than the President of the United States. I remember reading in China that the "traitor Tito, the proponent of revisionism, is using for his personal expenses dollars paid to him by his older brother, American imperialism" (apparently finding that the dinars he mercilessly squeezes out of the Yugoslav workers are not enough).

A speech that Marshal Chen Yi delivered at the Peking Hotel, which was heard by about fifty Soviet specialists, was devoted mainly to "the intrigues of American imperialism." I remember that Madame Chen, a woman of forty or so with neatly combed hair and an intelligent and sensitive face, watched her husband with a serious and intent expression, as he accused American imperialism of the seven deadly sins: "unleashing the Korean War," "grabbing Formosa," protecting the Kuomintang men who were trying to hold out there, opposing the liberation movements of the peoples of Asia, Africa, and Latin America, imposing the embargo on trade with China, blocking China's admission to the U.N., and refusing to extend diplomatic recognition to China. This last point seemed to bring Chen's fury to a climax, and he finished this part of his speech with a roar: "Since America does not recognize us, we do not recognize America!"

Despite my precarious health, I never missed a day of work during the 380 days I spent in China in 1958 and 1960. Still, I could not stay away from doctors altogether and once or twice had to pay them a visit.

My trouble in Peking was that I was deprived of even the half-hour walk I took regularly in Moscow, since I always had to travel by automobile. As a result of this lack of exercise, I suffered from a familiar complaint among elderly, and sedentary, people—namely, constipation. My friend T'ao recommended that I consult a certain Chinese doctor who lived in the old quarter of Peking. I went to see him as much out of curiosity as need, I must say.

Almost as soon as we arrived, an unexplained and anonymous woman sat us down, offered us glasses of tea, and asked us to wait. A few minutes later, the doctor himself entered, a rather plump man of fifty or so with a fresh complexion and graying, crew-cut hair. He asked T'ao a few questions, after which he invited me to show him my tongue. Then he simply took my pulse, without looking at his watch! That was the entire treatment. While it was going on, a young woman came in and sat down near us; the doctor said something to her, and she took over the pulse-taking, holding my wrist exactly as he had done. When she was through, the doctor exchanged a few words with her, casually lit a cigarette, and told T'ao that there was nothing wrong with me. He pulled at a thin sheet of paper, traced a couple of rows of ideograms on it, and handed it to T'ao. When I asked what I owed him, the doctor looked at me in great surprise and told me that I owed him nothing at all.

From the doctor, we went to a Chinese pharmacy. T'ao gave the prescription to the druggist who banged away at an abacus for a long while, calculating the price. Along with the medicine, I received a small ceramic saucepan with a lid: Apparently, I was to boil a spoonful of the medicine, dissolved in water, and take the infusion in this fashion, after it had cooled off.

I examined that medicine in the Institute lab and succeeded in isolating nine compounds in it. Later, when I took it, I found it to have an excellent effect, and, before I left for the Soviet Union, I even ordered a prepared concentrate to take home with me.

Just before I left Peking for good after my second stay there in 1960, I had a great deal of work and a great deal to worry about before my recall home.

My Chinese friends, who were always very considerate to me, displayed great concern for me during those difficult days and did everything they could to keep up my health and my courage. I was examined by a very experienced old Chinese doctor who prescribed a medicine for me, and, like many other things that were provided for me in China—lodging, transportation, etc.— it was given to me free of charge. Not only that, but it was remarkably effective and kept me in good shape during those troubled days.

Certain Chinese medicines were very popular among us visiting Russian specialists. "Tiger balm," for one, was very highly thought of, a liniment that was said to be a great help in dealing with rheumatism, headaches, etc. The Russians also often bought other medicine that contained reserpine, which reduces blood pressure. (Among other well-known Chinese medicines, there is one that is obtained from a certain kind of deer, whose horn contains a special substance that is also used as a tonic by Russian doctors.)

In fact, there was a great deal of talk and argument among the visiting Russians about Chinese medicine. Some praised it, saying it worked miracles, while others dismissed it as sheer quackery. (To support the latter view, by the way, one might cite the solemn pledge to conquer cancer in three years that Chinese doctors made to Mao Tse-tung in 1958. Six years have passed since then and cancer is still with us. The flippancy and absurdity of such a "pledge" becomes obvious when one remembers that since 1958, all serious research in China has virtually come to a stop.) But it seems to me that one should take a different attitude toward Chinese medicine. If we mean by science the sum total of human experience accumulated over the centuries and handed down from generation to generation, then much of Chinese medicine must be considered as having a scientific basis. In the course of centuries, Chinese doctors have established the sequence of certain phenomena occurring in the human organism and also the action upon that organism of various substances, mostly vegetable in origin, when it is beset by various diseases. European medicine, using the experimental method, overtook the once unequalled Chinese medical accomplishments. But it is still true that there is much of value in Chinese medicine; its achievements and methods should be tested experimentally, and the best of them, once they have passed the test of experiment, should be included in the corpus of general ("European," as it is called in China) medicine.

Whenever a fairly sizable group of Soviet specialists left for home, the Chinese government would organize a farewell dinner party for them. In the summer of 1958, such a banquet was held for about 300 men who were to leave at the end of July or the beginning of August. Then, at the beginning of the second week of August, the Institute organized a farewell tea party for me. As is usual on such occasions, there were numerous farewell speeches paying tribute to "the spirit of internationalism" and also to some fictitious virtues of the Soviet specialist M. A. Klochko. The chairman of the tea party read a letter from the President of the Chinese Academy of Sciences commending my services, and a communication from Premier Chou En-lai bestowing the medal of Sino-Soviet friendship upon me. (I brought both the letter and the medal with me to Canada.) When my turn came to speak, I began my speech in Russian and finished by saying a few words in Chinese. Although I had painstakingly prepared my remarks and had gone over them several times, my impossible pronunciation and complete disregard for the intonations of Chinese speech, which, despite my comparatively musical ear, I had never learned to distinguish, made it impossible for my hosts to make out more than a few isolated words of what I was trying to say. In any event, I thanked the members of my Institute for their cooperation and kind assistance and finished by wishing good health, the best of luck, and great prosperity to all those present.

I still had an unpleasant task to do—to rush around spending the money I had earned in China. Of the 530 yüan of my monthly salary, I had customarily spent about 110 on food, 60–70 on clothes, and 30 on laundry, newspapers, books, and other odd expenses, so I had about 300 yüan left over every month. Since I had already bought all the presents I wanted to take back to Russia, buying more things seemed to me a sheer waste of time.

My work in China had given me a certain feeling of satisfaction, but I was often depressed by the matter of this salary of mine. It seemed ethically wrong, I thought, to be getting twice as much pay as my Chinese colleagues, who had just about the same qualifications as I. On top of that, I was getting at least as much again back in the Soviet Union. Actually, I thought 200 yüan would have been a more than adequate sum to cover my expenses in Peking.

During my last conversation with Hua Shao-chun, I offered him part of my leftover money as a gift to the Institute, or for schools, the hospitals, or any worthy cause. But he absolutely refused.

So I organized a dinner celebration for my Chinese friends, and the Party organization of the Academy responded by giving a farewell party in my honor. The Institute was represented by Liu Ta-kang and Hua, its top Party representative. The rest of the guests were from the Academy: There was Wang Tao, the head of the Foreign Section; his deputy in charge of the Soviet specialists, the trim young lady with predatory, sparkling eyes called Madame Cheng, whom I had met on my very first day in Peking; and Tuh Chang-chen, the Academy's Party secretary.

At the table, the conversation kept turning on my work in China. My hosts were generous in their praise of me and they continually emphasized that they would appreciate it if I returned to China as soon as possible to resume my work with them: Everyone present expressed the opinion that I was needed at Peking's Research Institute of Chemistry. I replied that I felt it a great honor to serve the illustrious Chinese people to the best of my limited talents and abilities. But, I added, I was not a free agent, and the decision as to whether I was to be sent back to China or kept at home rested, to begin with, with the Soviet Academy of Sciences. If and when such an opportunity were offered me, however, I would gladly take advantage of it and place myself at the service of Chinese science once again.

The next day, Professor Liu and some other members of the Institute came to see me off at the airfield. Our farewells were very warm, and I felt certain then that I would see my Chinese friends again.

When I returned to Moscow, I immediately sat down to write my report on my work in China, and this was read at the Moscow Institute of General and Inorganic Chemistry.

Usually, reports on foreign trips by members of the Institute were divided into two parts: a brief summary of the work they had carried out—their participation in conferences and at learned meetings, etc.—and the much longer part of the report, their impressions of the country, life there, of the manners and mores of the people, even of their entertainments and "high life." Needless to say, the second part was always the more popular with the audience. Besides, photographs and postcards were usually passed around to illustrate this section.

I devoted my whole report, however, to my work in China, giving as an excuse for this departure from the usual procedure the fact that all the picturesque aspects of China had been fully covered in the report of our colleague N. P. Luzhnaya a year before.

Although my report produced a favorable impression on most of those present, it was violently attacked by the Old Wives' Committee of which Luzhnaya was such an important member. This hostility reached such a point that the routine resolution of thanks for the report was not passed. This illustrates once again the fact that, in the Soviet Union, it does not matter in the least whether a man does his job properly or not; what is infinitely more important is his relationship with the influential clique in his establishment, and this is true for all areas of human endeavor.

In 1959, a conference of chemists, called the Mendeleyev Congress, was finally held in Moscow, after having been postponed decade after decade. Professor Liu Ta-kang and Professor Yang of Tientsin came from China to attend it. They had to share a rather dark room in the Ukraine Hotel—and this at a time when a Soviet specialist in China was getting a pleasant room all to himself. I was furious that such prominent Chinese scientists should be treated so off-handedly. I and another professor who had worked in China went to see the official who was assigning quarters to the guests, and we told him in no uncertain terms what we thought of the treatment Liu and Yang had received. The fellow tried to justify what he had done, assuring us he had no idea who these Chinese were, that he had been under the impression they were rank-and-file delegates.

A few days later, a small dinner party was organized in one of the rooms of the Praha Restaurant in honor of our Chinese guests. The dinner was much scantier than the most modest meal ever offered to a Soviet specialist by the Chinese.

I took advantage of Professor Liu's visit, however, to send some presents to my Chinese friends who had, incidentally, done the same with their Russian colleagues.

Many Soviet citizens who had been in China kept up a correspondence with their former Chinese co-workers. On the whole, this contact was formal, consisting of notes expressing good wishes on certain traditional holidays—May Day, New Year's Day, or October 1 and November 7, the days of the Chinese and Russian Communist revolutions.

But these correspondences usually petered out after a few

months. There were some less official exchanges among those of us who had acquired true friends in China, but one could not be too frank in these letters because it was well known that mail between China and the Soviet Union was subject to a strict double censorship in each country.

PART TWO

China, 1960

CHAPTER NINE

I Return to China

I kept up my correspondence with my Chinese friends throughout the winter of 1958–59. Among other things, they gave me
to understand that the Chinese Academy of Sciences was making a
determined effort to have me sent back to China, and that all that
was wanting was permission from the Soviet authorities. My
Chinese friends had no doubts about my own willingness to
return to their country and wrote that they hoped to see me
again in the fall of 1959.

In the spring of that year, Committees on International Affairs
were formed in various establishments of the Soviet Academy of
Sciences, their function being to select candidates to send on
foreign assignments. Needless to say, the ladies' cabal in our
Institute had their ears to the ground, and as soon as the committees were formed, they managed to pack ours with their own
partisans.

A few months later, we received a document entitled "Plan
for Scientific Cooperation Between the Academies of Sciences
of the Soviet Union and the Chinese People's Republic in the
Field of Chemistry." In that document, I found my name in the sec-

tion on the "Study and Analysis of Rare Elements," and in the column marked "length of assignment," it said "two to three years" next to my name.

Names do not usually figure in these plans—only the degree and the specialty of the required expert. The fact that my name was indicated and my services requested for such an extensive period was a heavy blow to the Old Wives' Committee, who had spared no efforts to create the impression that my work in China had been unsatisfactory. But, when my case was examined at the meeting of our Foreign Committee, a strange reversal took place. All those who had been insistently trying to prove that my work in Moscow had been unsatisfactory suddenly began to praise it to the skies, arguing that the Institute could not afford to dispense with my services for such a long time, but that if the Chinese insisted, I could perhaps be allowed to leave for a maximum of three months.

Then one of the ladies expressed her surprise that the Chinese were requesting me as an expert on rare elements. "There must be some misunderstanding, surely?" I explained that the work the Chinese actually wanted me to do would be of a much broader scope but that I would do some special work on the enrichment with platinum metals of electrolytic residues of copper and nickel based on the research for which I had won the Stalin Prize in 1948.

"But you yourself, do you want to go to China?" the lady asked me.

"I am a small cog in a vast enterprise," I said diplomatically, and the decision is not up to me. If I am told to go, I will go. I only hope that I will be no less useful in China than many of our comrades who have also served there."

"But how could you leave your laboratory for two years?"

"Well, as a matter of fact, I couldn't," I said. "But I could very well leave for eight or ten months. I could prepare a plan of work with my assistants for that time, and I am sure they could manage with guidance from me by mail. When I came back, I could make a report on the work accomplished in my lab during my absence. I certainly do not think it would be useful for me to go to China for only three months—preparations alone would take up that much time before I could start on the work itself."

Nevertheless, the committee decided that I was to be sent to China for three months. A month later, a telegram arrived from Peking, signed by Wang Tao, the head of the Foreign Section of the Chinese Academy, which said: "We requested that Doctor M. A. Klochko be loaned to us for two or three years. You have authorized him to come to China for only three months. We request you once again to send him to China for at least one or two years. Kunming, the city of eternal spring, awaits him."

Our committee was summoned anew. Since the three-month leave of absence granted to me had already been entered in the contract, it was decided to send me to China for ten months if, at the end of the first three months, the Chinese requested my services for an additional seven.

The formalities for my trip were somewhat simpler than they had been for my first journey, but two innovations had been introduced since 1958—a new set of directives, and the censoring of my lectures in advance. The former was issued by the director of our Chemistry Institute in Moscow and outlined a complete program of activities for me in China, from which I was not allowed to depart. I was ordered to keep these two new details secret from both "our people and the Chinese" and never to show the directives to anyone but the Soviet frontier control.

It goes without saying that I decided immediately to ignore

these orders and to do whatever I considered most useful for Chinese science. Meanwhile, a colleague of mine at the Institute in Moscow had returned from a sojourn in China, and he reported that many scientists there were expecting my return, and that they expected me to be working in Kunming. On March 10, I began my return trip to China.

There is no natural demarcation line between the Chinese People's Republic and the Soviet Union. The same yellow-brown, snow-powdered steppe extends on both sides of the frontier. The Moscow-Peking train, which took me in eight days from one city to the other, passed under an iron-grille arch made of thin iron strips, and two Chinese frontier officials came into my compartment—one a civilian, the other a soldier. The civilian asked for my passport and said in Russian: "Since you are a specialist and have come to help us, we won't inspect your luggage." But they peeked into the boxes under my seat just as the Soviet frontier guard had done. I gathered that a period of "vigilance" was on.

Then I realized the extent of the new mistrust: The Russian nationals of Chinese origin on the train, who had already been subjected to outright requisition by Soviet customs, had to submit to another painful search by the Chinese officials.

At the railroad station in Peking, Professor Liu Ta-kang and Li Fu-teh were waiting for me, and we drove over to the Hotel Peking. (Since I was due to go to southern China and was not going to stay very long in town, the Friendship Hotel was not available for me: It is reserved for those who are to spend at least three months in the capital.)

In the Hotel Peking, besides the transient Soviet specialists, I saw some European businessmen, some swarthy South Americans, and several African Negroes, whose wives, wrapped in clouds of gaudy colored material, looked like strange exotic birds with bright green, blue, and yellow tails trailing behind them.

In the hotel bookshop, a young man who spoke quite good English offered me a catalogue of English-language publications. I examined it carefully, marking it at various points with a red pencil; the next day, fourteen books and pamphlets on various aspects of modern China, ranging from *A Short Course in Chinese Philosophy* to a Chinese-English phrase book were at my disposal to sweeten my evening leisure time in my hotel room.

The day after my arrival in Peking, several thousand people attended a meeting dedicated to Sino–Latin-American Friendship held in the new Palace of the People's Representatives. Li Fu-teh and I went to this meeting, which consisted of a speech followed by a concert. Between the two, an intermission was called, during which Li Fu-teh told me that I was one of a small group of Soviet and other guests (mostly citizens of the "People's Democracies") who had been invited to a reception given by Premier Chou En-lai. We passed through a succession of high-ceilinged rooms and finally reached a narrow marble hall. A few dozen guests were already waiting there, both men and women, from the Soviet Union, East Germany, Bulgaria, India, and other countries. Among the hosts I recognized Chou En-lai, Foreign Minister Chen Yi, and Peng Chen, the mayor of Peking and Secretary of the Central Committee of the CCP. The latter approached me, and we exchanged a few civilities. Chou En-lai and Chen Yi, meanwhile, sat at a table amidst a group of people of various nationalities; then we were all photographed. The next day, the *People's Daily* reported this reception and gave a complete list of the guests, beginning with my name.

Such receptions were quite usual in Peking in 1960. Delegations from every corner of the earth, from Japan and from Cyprus, from England and from Australia, not to mention the visitors from the Communist bloc, came and went every day. Instead of feeding and clothing their own people, instead of raising the material standards and cultural level of the Chinese people, the rulers of the People's Republic were trying to play politics on a world scale, and were spending substantial sums on the game.

On Monday, March 21, I drove to Peking's Research Institute of Chemistry where I had worked in 1958. The first thing that caught my eye was the two armed sentries at the Institute's door. I had never seen sentries there in 1958. Obviously, it was one of the consequences of the mad secrecy and security drive that began to sweep over China in the closing days of 1959 and that threatened to smother the frail sproutings of Chinese science timidly trying to break through the stony blocks of "The Struggle Against Rightwingers," the "Give One's Heart to the Party" campaign, etc. Now everything was "classified" and "confidential," and no one dared any longer even to say what kind of research he was engaged in.

Under the guise of "secrecy," frauds had their heyday in Chinese science. Now one could claim great results without doing anything, and reap honors and financial rewards. A somewhat similar state of affairs had existed in the Soviet Union during the last years of Stalin's rule, when practically every scientific communication was "classified," when a scientific paper had to pass through innumerable channels before it could be published in a professional journal and often disappeared before reaching its destination.

Now, in China, for instance, I was not allowed to attend a conference on the utilization of ocean and lake salts, although there could be nothing in this subject that could possibly be considered secret. Actually, the authorities at first invited me, informing me of the place and time when the conference was to be held, but later, some higher-ups decided that, although "Klochko is well-disposed toward China," he was nevertheless a Soviet specialist and should be kept at arms-length from anything that could give him an inkling about the state of any branch of Chinese industry—and this at a time when I was in charge of "classified research" in Kunming!

Within a week or so of my arrival, I familiarized myself with reports on various research projects carried out during 1959. I toured the labs, discussed the projects with my colleagues, and held a few consultations. I was very happy to see some of my old friends again, and many of them gave me a rousing welcome. Even in the library, Institute members got up from their seats and came over to shake my hand and tell me how delighted they were to see me again. Professor Liu's face still radiated that friendly smile, although many a silver strand had appeared in his hair. There was still the same sparkle of distrust in the eyes of Hua, the political director of the Institute. One woman scientist had given birth, during my absence, to a baby girl whom she proudly showed to me at the entrance to the Institute. But still, when I talked to all these friends, I felt a certain tension.

The section working on physical chemistry, so close to my heart, had been considerably expanded. Professor Huan Tzu-chin was now working full time for Peking University and it was the quiet and taciturn Po who ran the lab, a job he did with great skill. I did not find, however, that any notable achievements had been made, despite the fact that a lot of new equipment had been received from the Soviet Union and East Germany. But there was no doubt in my mind that if the scientists had been left alone to pursue their work, they would have had something to show for their efforts during the eighteen months since I had left China.

One day, Professor Liu came to my hotel with a few representatives of the Academy of Sciences to discuss future research plans for various chemistry establishments. At the same time, he informed me that someone from the Kunming Institute of Metallurgy and Ceramics would come to Peking to meet me.

The next morning, Li Fu-teh came to my hotel room with Madame Cheng, who was in charge of the Soviet specialists and whom I had met in 1958. She had at that time promised to give me Chinese lessons in exchange for Russian lessons, and, having forgotten all about it, was surprised to see a teach-yourself Chinese book on my desk. So I reminded her of her old promise, and her feline eyes lit up. She would, of course, have been delighted to help me out with my Chinese, but with all her duties, including those to her three children. . . .

While we were talking, a young man wearing a tan jacket came into the room. There was something about his face, with his bulging forehead and thinning hair that made me think of the mandarins and wise men on old Chinese vases and etchings. Intelligence radiated from his wide-open eyes. He was the man from Kunming who had come to see me.

The man from Kunming proceeded to inform me right away of the Institute's desiderata in regard to research. He enumerated the subjects of which they hoped I would take charge. I told him that the matters he had listed were most interesting and that I was prepared to advise on some of them and take charge of others. But, I added, he had mentioned something like twenty-five or thirty topics, each of them quite involved, and that any one of them would take a team of four to five scientists and several assistants one or two years to handle. If all of them were done, or most of them, the entire research staff of a large institute would be completely absorbed for many years.

After a brief discussion, we agreed to decide on a list of the most pressing topics. We planned to collect the necessary literature on these subjects, as well as equipment for the lab, and leave for Kunming in a few days.

CHAPTER TEN

First Impressions of Kunming

In 1958, I had made the Moscow-Peking and return trips by air, while inside China I had traveled by rail. In 1960, it was just the reverse, mostly because my main bases during the year, Peking and Kunming, were not yet connected by rail.

We left the hotel before daybreak and breakfasted at the airport, where I saw a group from the staff of the Soviet Academy of Sciences, including Professor Boky, deputy chairman of the Foreign Section of the Academy, Professor Kiselev, and others, who had just arrived from North Vietnam where they had gone to organize a research center.

Three men awaited us in Kunming: Tan Lin-chin, the director of the Institute, a man of forty or so with the sensitive face of an intellectual; his deputy, who had the coarse features of a Chinese working man; and Chiang Min-pao, the bespectacled but goodlooking interpreter.

Tan started talking to me in Chinese, through the interpreter, but he quickly shifted to English when I asked him if he spoke it; he told me he had spent about ten years in the United States. I noticed that during the whole conversation, his deputy never uttered a word, but simply kept an eye on me in silent watchfulness. I was to meet this man many times without even hearing him speak, and at one point I began to think he was dumb. I had to wait until my last evening in Kunming, at the end of July, before I really heard the sound of his voice.

The welcoming threesome at the airport drove me first to the hotel in Kunming. There I was given two large and airy rooms: For the first time in my life, I had a bedroom and separate sitting room all my own. Each room had a balcony and wide window with a view of the lake, the park of Yünnan University, and beyond them, the distant mountains.

I settled into these comfortable quarters, and soon discovered that a welcoming party was to be held that evening in honor of my arrival. And a splendid party it was indeed: I even removed my self-imposed restrictions against alcoholic beverages and second helpings of good Chinese food! The atmosphere was gay and relaxed, there was much laughter, and we all chattered away in Chinese, Russian, and English.

Kunming is the capital of Yünnan Province, a province that borders on Laos, Vietnam, and Burma. The last province to be integrated into China, it is still one with a population of remarkably diverse national and racial origins.

Most of Yünnan is mountainous, less than 10 per cent of the land being suitable for agriculture, but to make up for this, the province is rich in sources of power: The Yangtze alone, with its immense falls, within the boundaries of the province, provides a large share of hydraulic power. This power, combined with rich mineral resources, gives Yünnan a solid basis for industrial development, particularly in the metallurgical field.

Kunming itself lies at an altitude of 6,400 feet above sea level, near a sizable lake. The Yangtze flows past Kunming about 60 miles north, and a tributary of the huge river passes very close to the city. About 120 miles south, almost on the Tropic of Cancer, begins the jungle.

Provincial capital though it is, Kunming has none of the marks of a city planned for such an administrative purpose. Indeed, Kunming seems built on no plan at all. But the abundance of trees and bushes along its streets, the view from any point within it of the bluish mountains in the distance—these and other factors make Kunming attractive in any case, and its temperate climate is another pleasant aspect of its charm. In 1960, we had no rain to speak of until late in June, when thunderstorms and heavy rains began, reaching their greatest intensity in July.

The Kunming plain is really the bottom of an ancient lake which gradually became silted up. The battle still rages between man and the water, however, and the rice paddies, which extend to the very edge of the nearby lake, must be protected by dams and levees. Immediately around Kunming, these flat plain rice fields stretch as far as the eye can reach, and the opposite shore of the lake is veiled in blue mist. But in the middle distance, one can see wooded hills with meadows and gardens on their slopes, and the smooth-flowing tributary of the Yangtze; then, far away, on the horizon, the high, blue mountains.

On the first morning of my stay in Kunming, Professor Tan came to pick me up at the hotel, and we drove to the Institute through streets bordered by high fences and along a narrow canal of stagnant green water. We entered a courtyard and alighted at the gateway to the Institute's main building. From the gate to the door of the Institute, the members—more than a hundred people—were lined up on either side of the driveway to greet me.

The grounds of the Institute offered a strange picture in contrasts, appearing like the battleground of a struggle between two forces, one making the land beautiful and the other bringing chaos into the entire scene. In various corners, now one, now the other force seemed to have triumphed. By the main building, there was a charming little garden and nearby, a shaded *allée* between huge, old trees; farther on, the fields began, and on the skyline one could see the soft outline of Serpent Mountain, with its three beautiful conical summits. Even the vegetable garden was pretty, with its even green patches and surrounding pink bushes. But nearby, there were heaps of broken crockery and piles of straw and pieces of wood, bottles containing acids standing open near a pigsty, and, not far off, an open cesspool.

I was given a large, bright room for a temporary office while I was working at the Institute. On the same day, the director, Tan, came to see me there, and, as we sat sipping tea, he told me the history of the establishment to which most of my efforts were to be devoted during my 1960 visit to China.

The Institute had been founded in the early 1930's by Professor Chou Jen (whom I had met in 1958), the director of the Shanghai Institute of Metallurgy and Ceramics, as a branch of the latter. He had worked here during the Japanese occupation of Shanghai. (At the entrance to the main building, where my office was located, there was a marble plaque written by Chou himself in commemoration of the foundation of the Institute.)

Now, the Institute is no longer a branch of the one in Shanghai, but an independent research center specializing in the study of processes connected with the mining and refinement of nonferrous metals, in which Yünnan Province is one of the richest areas in China. The Institute became independent in 1959.

Its working parts were divided into five sections, which studied rare metals, metallography (the study of the structure and properties of metals and alloys), the enrichment of ores, ceramics, and analytical chemistry. In the entire Institute, there were at most a score of persons with a higher education, and perhaps only half of them had any research experience. Among the latter, of course, was the director, a specialist in metallography, and Che, the man who had come to meet me in Peking and who was a former elementary school teacher. He had taught himself chemistry and also English, so that he could read the literature. I don't know whether he had any official diploma of higher education, but this is quite irrelevant since in any case Chinese students in recent years have had a great deal of propaganda stuffed into their heads but little opportunity to acquire true knowledge. It appeared that Che had received a good basic education and was well read in Chinese history and literature.

Madame He, a quite efficient lady, was in charge of the analytical chemistry lab. Aside from her, only two persons with advanced training worked there. The rest of the Institute scientists were without any university-level training or speciality and had at best a secondary or trade-school education. The case of the "tall girl" was a characteristic instance of the way scientists are trained in China.

Often, on crossing the courtyard on my way to the labs, I passed a girl who was much taller than any other person in the Institute, man or woman. I asked my interpreter about her, and he told me that she was only sixteen (I would have said she was at least twenty) and that she had worked as a cleaning girl in the Kunming branch of the Academy of Sciences, where it had been discovered that she had unusual ability. So she was sent to the Institute to do research work. It never occurred to anyone that, if she really had unusual talents, she should have been sent first to complete her high-school education. I suggested this course of action to my colleagues, arguing that only with a diploma and then a specialized study of chemistry at the university level should she go on to do research work, if, by that time, she still displayed talent. Such a procedure, however, appeared much too slow and painful to my audience. The tall girl, they felt, could be of use to science right now. I don't know how they could have deduced this from the way she manipulated a broom.

The tall girl herself did not worry about scientific training either. Indeed, she was quite cool toward science altogether. I rarely met her in the labs, but almost every time I peeked out of my window, I could see her playing ball with a group of young men. In the ball games, her natural assets—her stature and her long arms—gave her an obvious advantage, so that she constantly outscored her male partners. She would look at them out of her narrowed eyes with the indulgence of a mother cat watching her kittens playing with a ball of wool. The girl did have an intelligent face, though, and it is quite possible that one day she might have become a good scientist. It was certainly unlikely in the conditions under which talent was being picked out in China. We must understand, however, that in a country where an official slogan is "Every Citizen Must Participate in Scientific Progress," despite the fact that 75 per cent of those citizens are illiterate, such instances are bound to occur.

I should in all fairness say a few words about my interpreter, who played in Kunming a more important part in my daily life than did my interpreters in Peking, where the staff of the hotel understood Russian.

Of above average height for a Chinese, with a rather rounded face and full dark eyes, Chiang Min-pao was an extremely handsome Oriental, which is why he was sent to a film studio soon after he was graduated from the Russian Language Institute in Shanghai. He quickly took a dislike to life in the Chinese movie world, however, and quit it after a few months. But the time he did spend in the studios seemed to have been useful, insofar as it improved his attire and general mien. He somewhat resembled

Kuo Mo-jo, but the latter, a man whose experiences were incomparably more complex and profound, had a more expressive smile.

In the course of his short-lived film career, Min-pao had also become an accomplished dancer, and every Saturday night he was to be seen whirling in the main ballroom of our hotel. Otherwise, he did not seem to have the serious knowledge one might expect in a young man of his age and education.

I knew that Min-pao was married and once I asked him where his wife was.

"She is teaching Russian in a village school in another province. She will join me at the end of the school year, because there is an opening for someone who knows Russian in the administration of the Kunming branch of the Academy." Obviously, he awaited her with great impatience.

Once he came to work in a state of utter dejection and would hardly talk. I abstained from asking him what the matter was, but later that evening, as we were strolling along the shore of the lake, he told me of his problem.

His wife had been given leave to come to Kunming for a month to make arrangements for her employment there. She was told that if she found a job, she would be authorized to remain with her husband permanently. But literally a few seconds before her train was due to start, a messenger handed her an order to get off: The authorities of the town had decided that she must conduct a summer Russian-language course for adults. And so, poor Min-pao was not to see his wife at all that summer. On top of it all, he was worried about her health, for she was not very strong, and the food situation was considerably worse in the town where she worked than in Kunming.

From time to time, Min-pao helped me out in my spasmodic efforts to learn Chinese. The Chinese spoken in Kunming is closer to that spoken in Peking than the Chinese one hears in

Shanghai or Canton, and so I could sometimes make myself understood to people who did not know any Russian. I would ask them about their private lives and their family affairs, using up my limited stock of Chinese words in the process.

Min-pao had a list of instructions on how a Chinese interpreter attached to a foreign specialist should behave. He was not supposed to sit next to the foreigner while driving, for instance. I never knew how strictly he followed these instructions or what sort of reports he wrote on my behavior and on what I said, but, probably because of his inherent charm and tact, I never felt he was a watchdog.

Chiang Min-hua was my other, technical translator, who worked with me in the laboratory and in my lectures. He was quite a different type, a very clever student who was doing postgraduate work at the local technical college. Min-hua was quite adequate for translating my lectures and consultations, and he was also satisfactory in helping me with my lectures on general chemistry that I gave at Yünnan University to an audience of 250 students. Although he performed all these duties competently, and held a teaching post at the local Polytechnical Institute as well, he felt acutely that he needed more study and hoped to go for this purpose to the U.S.S.R. I do not know whether he ever realized that dream, but I am certain that, given a fair chance, he would have made a first-class scientist.

In the laboratory under my charge, Che was the senior Chinese and Liu Tien-chang was his assistant. Liu was strikingly thin and always looked dejected, which was understandable, considering that he, his wife, four children, and an old mother had to live on the 70 yüan a month he was paid by the Institute plus only 40 yüan earned by his wife. Although food is cheap in China, and the 110 yüan would go further than the $44 they represent at the official rate of exchange, it is difficult to feed, lodge, and clothe a family of seven on that sum. Food for one costs at least 20 yüan a month.

Later, during a trip to Peking we took together, when I came to know Liu better, I realized that his material hardships had not prevented him from developing high moral qualities—industriousness, honesty, friendliness, and a strong sense of human dignity.

My work at Kunming consisted in finding approprate methods for the refinement of the by-products of nonferrous metals. Six men worked with me in the laboratory, and, when analysis was required, it was done at an analytical lab directed by Madame He. I also lectured at the University and organized lab discussions. In the course of this work, I gave four lectures on problems of the metallurgy of precious metals to my collaborators, instead of the one that the directives issued to me in Moscow had ordered. Not only did I direct the other men's lab work, but I often did some of the experiments myself, which was a great joy, since in Moscow I had had little opportunity to do lab work.

Although we spent most of our time in these two labs, we also availed ourselves of a small-scale and rather rudimentary foundry that stood on the banks of an irrigation canal just outside the Institute building. I would work away in my study, going to the window from time to time to keep an eye on the operation from there, ready to rush over if I thought my presence was needed.

Our work progressed well and my men worked very hard. The whole operation was tiring, however, for the installation required round-the-clock attention, and it was also important that everyone be at their most alert. Whenever anyone was absent from the lab, the reason was his attendance at some of those senseless political meetings, which were, of course, still going on. Tiring of this incessant excuse, I told the men that attendance at the meetings was not going to help us in our work and that if

I could not have their full-time services, I could not guarantee success. We finally agreed on a *modus vivendi* by which, on every day but Saturday—set apart by the authorities especially for the study of political science—there must be a certain required number of persons attending the instruments. And so, although it was slower than I had hoped, we made some progress.

One day, I realized that something was going wrong in an experiment, and discovered that parts of our intricate apparatus had been left unattended for some time. It turned out that the person assigned to it had fallen asleep during his night shift because meetings held during the day had prevented him from getting any sleep.

"We'll give him a going-over at a disciplinary meeting," Che suggested.

I begged him to abandon this plan and to see to it instead that the night-shift men have time to sleep during the day.

It is true that I found more people working, in the lab or at their desks, than I had in Peking in 1958, but it was still by and large true that the higher a man's training and the more responsible his position, the more time he was forced to waste at meetings. Che wasted more time than his assistant, Liu; and as for the director, he was away from the Institute for days on end.

Once or twice a week, members of my Institute came to my hotel after dinner to consult me or talk over various questions. But usually I had the evenings to myself, and I spent them studying Chinese, reading Chinese history, literature, and philosophy, doing my utmost to understand the people among whom I was living. And I also indulged in one activity that is criminal from the Soviet point of view: I listened to the foreign radio. I managed to hear many English-language broadcasts and even an anti-Soviet Russian program broadcast by a radio station that called itself "Baikal." This was a treat, because in the Soviet Union, foreign Russian-language broadcasts are almost completely jammed.

The library of the Kunming Institute had only technical books, so I had to go elsewhere for the books that filled my evenings, and for papers and magazines. In the park across from my hotel was the provincial public library, and in it I found a better selection of foreign publications than in Moscow where, in 1961, one could find only three foreign Communist newspapers—the East German *Neues Deutschland,* the French *L'Humanité* and the Italian *Unitá*—on the newsstands.

The librarian at the public library, whose name was Sha, was a tall, spare, middle-aged man who was fluent in Chinese, Vietnamese, French, and English, and who could also read Russian, German, and Japanese. In the course of fifty years of using public libraries, I had never met such a competent and friendly librarian. When I asked him for a book, he seemed able to find it in seconds if it was available at all. If it was not, he would advise me as to the best substitute for it that would yield the information I wanted. (I also got into the habit of looking over the new books regularly once a week, which was a great pleasure for me.)

It turned out that Sha's great proficiency in French was due to his having been educated in a mission school in Indochina, where he had spent many years. It is quite possible that he himself was of Indochinese origin.

Once, lecturing on the use of chemical literature in research, I pointed out the importance of having a good library run by a competent, devoted librarian, and I cited Comrade Sha as an example. An audible murmur of surprise ran through the audience as soon as I mentioned his name. Soon after, Che explained all: Everyone who bore the name Sha, he said, was a Kuomintang man.

Later, I had good grounds to believe that my public praise had done Sha very poor service. At the beginning of July, he suddenly vanished. When I inquired about him, his assistant was embarrassed and flustered. She told me, however, that he had been sent to work on the land for a few months. I am inclined to think that a man with a suspect name, praised, in addition, by a Soviet specialist who was himself suspect (as all Soviet citizens were at that time), automatically became a victim of the agents of the Chinese security police.

One of Tan's assistants combined his duties at the Institute with the position of Party secretary at the local normal school. He invited me once to visit the establishment for whose ideological guidance he was responsible. My tour began with a survey of the labs.

Now, in all schools where analytical chemistry is taught, the students learn methods of detecting and determining the chemical elements. Usually at least twenty or twenty-five of the most common elements and groups are studied. But at the Kunming normal school, it had been decided to discard this bourgeois method, which, by the way, is used not only in the "imperialist" United States but also in the "socialist" Soviet Union. The normal school had tailored analytical chemistry to its own ideological liking. Since there are large copper deposits in the mines of Yünnan Province, their reasoning went, why should one bother to take all that time to study methods of qualitative analysis? Their purpose would be served as soon as students were capable of determining copper and nothing more, both qualitatively and quantitatively. Of course, one could ask the thorny, albeit obvious, question, "What if the Yünnan ore deposits contain lead, nickel, selenium, tellurium, or other elements, in addition to copper?" The answer one would probably receive would be, "Even if these elements are present, a person asking such a question displays a distrust of the abilities of the masses as well as a weakness for bourgeois thinking and is guilty of revisionism."

One can imagine that the quality of instruction in the teaching of analytical chemistry was therefore not high in the normal school. A girl in one research lab was investigating a problem that had been solved long before in Peking, but she was not aware of that fact because of the system of classifying ordinary scientific information. A young man was working on compounds of alkali metal but had no idea of what had been done previously in the field. In this case, the mania for secrecy had nothing to do with it, for everything about this matter had been published and was available in English, Russian, French, and German. But the greatest surprise awaited me in one section of the normal school where about fifteen students were sitting around a large table cluttered with books and papers, writing and arguing hotly about something.

"What are they doing?" I asked.

"Preparing a textbook on organic chemistry."

"Who are they? Teachers? Graduate students?"

"No, they are second-year students. They are just beginning to study organic chemistry, and they are writing their textbook as they go along."

"Why? Are there no organic chemistry textbooks in Chinese?"

"There is one, written by some teachers at Peking University, but it isn't suited to our needs. The students use it, but they are trying to adapt it to the conditions of Yünnan Province."

"Are the laws of organic chemistry different in Yünnan and Peking?" I wanted to know.

I received no answer to that question.

After completing our inspection tour, we returned to the reception hall, where I answered written and oral questions. Some of the questions were serious and to the point, but they were drowned out in an avalanche of inane or thoughtless queries: What's the use of thermodynamics? Is it possible to do without mathematics in the natural sciences? Can mathematics be adapted to the needs of the building of socialism? When the flood of questions had exhausted itself—I coped with them directly one by one—I was asked to express my "highly competent opinion" on the normal school.

I told them. I did not try to pass over anything in polite silence, but gave them my sincere opinion. I told them I was greatly surprised to learn that people who taught physics and chemistry thought they could do so without any idea of thermodynamics and that others of them wanted to do away with mathematics, the basis of every natural science. I said that no research should be undertaken without a thorough study of the literature on the subject, otherwise time was bound to be wasted on "rediscovering America after Columbus."

I pointed out that a student trained in their method of analysis, faced with a piece of Yünnan ore containing a small quantity of silver, would never find the precious metal because he would only be able to recognize copper. Lastly, I expressed the utmost indignation on the subject of the textbook which the beginning students in organic chemistry were preparing: "This is not only a waste of time: It is downright harmful. Instead of humbly studying a new discipline, these students will imagine that they know more organic chemistry than their instructors or professors. Why don't you, by the same token, ask children in the first grade, who know only a few odd ideograms, to compose textbooks of the Chinese language? Is it possible that there are no qualified Chinese specialists who would be able to prepare competent textbooks, provided they were allowed enough time to do the work?"

My hosts were obviously bewildered and taken aback by such unfriendly utterances from their guest. The Party secretary who had invited me there became gloomier and gloomier as Min-hua dispassionately translated my criticisms. But even the rest of them were so shocked that they could not muster the indispensable Chinese grin as they saw me off. On the way back I asked Min-hua whether he thought I had been too blunt.

"Oh," he said, "serves them right! They know that what they're doing is fairly worthless, even if they put on pompous airs. They know it's all a waste of time and human resources."

After this incident, the invitation I had received to visit the Polytechnic Institute was withdrawn, apparently out of fear that my shocking behavior at the normal school would be repeated.

I may say, however, that the normal school had all that was physically needed to make a good school. It had light and spacious classrooms, adequate equipment in some of the labs, and an observatory that was not bad at all. But it lacked the one necessary ingredient: the earnest will to give the students a serious education. And the students lacked a serious will to study.

The things that impressed me most about the normal school were the splendid cabbages growing in the gardens. Obviously much love and care and effort had been expended on those cabbages, unlike the teaching process.

Judging by the literature on the subject, China is not rich in the ores of precious metals—gold, silver, or platinum. This makes it necessary to obtain these metals during the electrolytic purification of copper, nickel, and other nonferrous metals whose ores contain them in certain admixtures.

At present, probably more than 10 per cent of all the gold obtained in the world comes from the electrolytic processing of copper, and, by the same token, most platinum and kindred metals are obtained during the electrolytic processing of nickel. In view of China's relative wealth in copper ore, its processing could have become an important source of gold and silver; similarly, when the projected nickel refining plants begin operation they will yield a certain amount of the platinum metals—perhaps not enough for export but possibly enough to satisfy domestic demands. (So far, China has imported platinum metals.)

In Kunming, there was a copper processing plant that produced 5,000 tons of copper a year, and this capacity could have been expanded tenfold. The amount of gold and silver obtained from the electrolytic refinement of 50,000 tons of copper ore that contains a few hundredths or thousandths of 1 per cent of gold or silver, is not inconsiderable. But getting precious metals as a "by-product" depends on fulfilling certain conditions, and these conditions were not fully met in Kunming. The whole operation still required considerable research.

Work on a huge electric furnace for smelting copper began in Kunming in the spring of 1960. The assemblage and testing of such furnaces must be done with great care and thoroughness, for the slightest oversight can cause terrible accidents. The furnaces use high-voltage and high-amperage currents, and the least false move in the installation, the smallest error in checking could result in the death of many workers. Warnings to this effect were voiced by an elderly and experienced Soviet engineer who was in charge of the whole operation, but the factory management was in a great hurry, anxious to have the furnace in operation by some revolutionary anniversary or other. They could not make it for May Day, and so they decided to open the furnace on July 1, the date of the founding of the Chinese Communist Party, although that date also was impractical from a technical point of view.

During the drying and testing of the furnace, the presence of engineers, skilled workers, and laborers was required round-the-clock. But, at one point, the furnace was left unattended for several hours, and it turned out that it had received the wrong amount of current. Work on the furnace had to be stopped forthwith, but no one was there to see to it: Everyone was off at a meeting. Luckily, the Soviet engineer arrived in time to save the furnace from a major breakdown. The incident caused a further postponement of the opening date because of damage to the parts.

The most important feature of this incident is the desertion by the shift on duty of the object entrusted to its supervision, for it sheds light on human behavior in China today. The flood of words about Communist responsibility, enthusiasm, and patriotism is nothing but unmitigated falsehood. In reality, there is no such thing in China as the feeling of ordinary human responsibility. Perhaps this is because there, as in the Soviet Union, everything is drowned by one overriding preoccuption—or fear; fear of what may happen to you today, tomorrow, or right now. The fear of being punished for failing to attend a political meeting today thus becomes stronger than the fear of causing tomorow the loss of a furnace worth hundreds of thousands of dollars.

During the assembly and testing of that furnace, some fatal accidents did occur. But in China today, just as always, human life is not valued very highly.

In 1958, a great to-do was raised by the Chinese press when thirty or forty roadbuilders came down with food poisoning. The newspapers wrote about medicines being flown to the sick men, about the virtues Mao and the Communist Party had shown in their paternal concern for the poisoned workers. And finally, to make the happy ending complete, persons "responsible" for the poisoning were unmasked, and, as might be expected, they turned out to be "members of families of the hostile classes." No one in his senses, of course, had any doubt that the poisoning was simply due to unsanitary food; nor were there any medical-legal documents produced specifying the poison used. (The whole affair reminded me very much of events in the Soviet Union under Stalin.) But when many Chinese workers died of lead and mercury poisoning in the mines of Yünnan Province in 1960, no mention of it appeared in the Chinese press, because it was very difficult in that case to find a "class enemy" to be blamed for it. And so the story was reported in whispers by the Soviet specialists who were present when it happened.

The Kunming copper plant had had a research lab attached to it, but this lab was now completely independent, doing work on the production of various chemicals. When I visited it, I noticed that this work was done in most unsanitary conditions. The people working with poisonous compounds did not even wear the gauze masks I saw on Peking traffic policemen; the flue and the ventilation system did not work. One room had been turned into a sort of exhibition hall in which about five hundred samples of the substances obtained in the plant were displayed. But I came to the conclusion that because of the lack of training and the poor condition of the equipment, it would be impossible efficiently to obtain even one-tenth of the substances on display.

In the analytical chemistry section, a large container of distilled water stood on a shelf, with pipes running from it that supplied water to the tables. The director pointed it out to me and said proudly: "See, that is a result of our campaign for a technological revolution. Our chemists no longer have to cross the whole room to get some distilled water: it is supplied directly to the spot where they work."

Then he showed me another "achievement of the technological

revolution"—a shaker for solutions that could shake two solutions simultaneously. In other countries, such adjustments of apparatus are made daily without it ever occurring to anyone to call them proof of a "technological revolution," but in China, the local newspapers greeted these minor improvements as revolutionary achievements.

However, I cannot blame the director and his associates for this naive boasting. After the Peking authorities had announced the nation-wide "campaign for a technological revolution," the government expected Chinese technology to evolve, not gradually in the course of several years, but within a month or two at a *revolutionary* pace. What else could the poor lab director do, under the terrible pressure of his local Party organization, which was constantly demanding proof that he actively participate in the campaign.

On the smoke-infested premises, darkened at all times by clouds of poisonous chemical dust, the management had opened a sort of technical chemistry school, and, what is even worse, they had built a dormitory there for forty of its pupils.

The workers in this laboratory, as in thousands of such establishments all over China, were trying to produce everything they could out of every raw material they might lay their hands on, without regard to economic considerations or common good sense. When extracting certain quantities of lithium from a kind of mica, for instance, they decided while they were at it to extract the potassium that was also present in small amounts, but thought nothing of using for this operation chemical reagents that cost ten times more than the potassium which they thus obtained and which could have been extracted from sea water much more easily and less expensively. Then, once the product was claimed by the establishment as an "achievement," all interest in it was lost. I used to see bottles of acids, piles of salts, reagents, and chemical apparatus heaped up in the yards under the open skies, under clouds of dust, exposed to the rain, spoiling, absorbing water —once these things had been used for the "campaign," no one could work up the slightest interest, let alone "enthusiasm," in them. All I could do was to advise the management to concentrate on ten or, at most, fifteen products for which there was a guaranteed supply of raw materials and a real demand. I repeatedly suggested that they also endeavor to improve the quality of their products and the working conditions of their labor force.

I could not possibly describe in this short book all the natural beauties and magnificent historical monuments I saw around Kunming, but I cannot resist saying a few words about the Copper Temple, one of the most interesting Buddhist temples I visited in China.

The Copper Temple is located about eighteen miles from the city, past a large settlement of slum-like houses—a community for the many ethnic minorities of Yünnan. The houses resemble the usual Chinese dwellings except that they are not whitewashed, which makes them look poor and shabby. Men and women with sunken cheeks and lusterless eyes were sitting on a low stone fence along the road, staring at our car as we drove by. Even the vegetation looked bleak and the grass worn thin. The Chinese who accompanied us spoke of the entire settlement with the utmost scorn.

Eventually, we drove into the courtyard of the Copper Temple. On either side of the driveway stood a dining hall and dormitories, and directly ahead, standing on a small elevation, was the temple itself—rather small, its walls built of copper plates etched with beautiful designs. The doors, also of copper, were latticed in a complicated pattern; the roof, whose eaves swept out beyond the walls, was supported by copper columns that made a sort of exterior arcade around the temple walls. Inside, I found three large and beautiful statues of Buddha and two of his disciples— all of them in copper, of course. The metal had a dark greenish patina of incomparable richness that somehow gave to the whole structure an added look of strength and solidity.

April 22, 1960, was the ninetieth anniversary of Lenin's birth, a date celebrated that year with far greater emphasis in China than in the Soviet Union.

I had received an invitation—on a postcard with a picture of a somewhat mongolized Lenin wearing a cloth cap—to attend a memorial meeting at the municipal theater that day, so I, together with a dozen Soviet and a few Czech specialists, and their wives, foregathered in the foyer of the theater. The top government officials of Yünnan Province and from Kunming were also there. When the bell rang to announce the beginning of the meeting, we visiting specialists were invited to sit on the stage with the presidium.

The meeting was opened by a man I had already noticed in the foyer because he was so strikingly fat—indeed, he was the fattest Chinese I had ever seen. He was the secretary of the Yünnan Province Party committee—i.e., the number one Party man in the area. It was clear that in his exalted position, this man was not in the least affected by the food shortage.

I understood virtually nothing of the fat man's speech, although I could realize the significance of the moments when he would turn reverently to the huge portrait of Lenin standing on the stage. From time to time, the audience clapped, but most of the people looked rather bored, some even closed their eyes, and I noticed heads dipping now and again. After the speech, we were given an opportunity to acquaint ourselves with the text of this opening oration and the others that had followed it: Each Soviet specialist received a beautiful edition of a book in Russian entitled *Long Live Leninism!* (I believe that a similar book in English was published simultaneously in Peking. Later, in Peking, I was given yet another copy of the Russian edition.) Exactly the same texts, taken from this book, were heard on that April 22 in all the towns and villages of China, from Harbin to Canton.

Long Live Leninism!, it turned out, was an extremely important document: the famous issue of *Red Flag* (the Chinese Communist Party organ) that represented Mao's first bomb tossed at the Kremlin's ideological ramparts. The statements in *Red Flag* are now well known to all those who have followed the history of the Sino-Soviet ideological rift. The authors try, by quoting Lenin, to prove that imperialism, represented primarily by the United States, has not really changed, and that as long as it survives, world wars are inevitable—from which it follows that imperialism is to be exterminated by force of arms. Needless to say, however, *Red Flag* did not pass over Enemy Number Two: The "Yugoslav revisionist clique" headed by the "spy Tito" was presented as a "loyal lieutenant of arch-imperialist America."

Coming more directly to the point, *Red Flag* also attacked the developments that had taken place in the Soviet Union after Stalin's death. It singled out the theory of peaceful coexistence, the statement made by Soviet leaders to the effect that war could be avoided, and the doctrine of a peaceful transition to socialism that is supposed to take place in some bourgeois countries.

Among other things, this book caused the Soviet authorities in China a considerable amount of extra work, for Embassy officials closely questioned each Soviet specialist in China as to whether he had received a copy of it and whether he had ever looked at it. Soviet customs officials even asked every Soviet citizen returning from China whether he had ever had the book in his hands at any time. Obviously, Soviet indignation over *Red Flag* was not due to the actual contents of the book, which could easily be dismissed as foolish, but to the fact that it represented the first open attempt by the Chinese government to advocate its own views in contrast to those of the Soviet Union. It was understandable that the Soviet government was particularly upset that the Chinese had made such a special effort to distribute copies of the document to Soviet citizens in China.

CHAPTER ELEVEN

New Currents

To carry out my work in the Kunming Institute, I needed not only residues obtained from the refining of copper, which I could get in Kunming, but also those from the electrolytic refining of nickel. And so it was decided that I should go to Shanghai, Peking, and Mukden to search for them. Besides, I needed some books on the subject and hoped to find them in Peking.

So Liu Tien-chang and I took off for Chungking, the first stop on the way to Peking.

Liu was no interpreter. He knew only a few dozen Russian words and not many more in English. We communicated in four languages—Chinese, of which I now knew several hundred words; Russian, which I was teaching him; English, of which he had a reading knowledge; and sign language and even drawings. Still, we understood each other well, and, in any case, I could not have dreamed of a pleasanter or more considerate traveling companion. For my part, I tried to inconvenience him as little as possible during our travels.

At about 2 P.M., we landed at the Chungking airport, where we were informed that the plane was going no farther that day. So we decided to visit the town. The distance from the airfield to the city itself is about 15 miles as the crow flies, but the drive is actually much longer, the road twisting and turning up and down mountain slopes. I had the impression that we often were retracing our steps when, after a quarter of an hour, the same panorama would once again open up before our eyes. But, each time, we were several hundred meters lower. . . . At last, the city appeared in front of us.

Chungking is a superb city in a country where remarkable towns are not rare. Situated at the junction of the Yangtze Kiang, the longest river in China and one of the greatest in the world, and of one of its most important tributaries, the Kia-ling, the heart of the city lies on a high peninsula above the rivers and spreads out along the banks of both, the houses and tree-lined streets atop the steep banks forming a beautiful pattern.

Grounded in Chungking for three days in bad weather, we finally took off in a driving rain, and, after a brief stop-over at Sian, reached Peking.

Liu and I wandered about at the Peking airfield for a long time —there was no one there to meet us. I asked him whether he was sure his wire announcing our arrival would have been received in time, and he assured me it must have been, and that in fact he had wired several times. As we were walking along a corridor in the terminal, Liu stopped a girl we passed and inquired if she had seen a representative from the Academy of Sciences anywhere. By a strange coincidence, she herself was the appointed representative; she was a technical member of the Academy. Liu had difficulty understanding her because she was a Korean.

I was most puzzled by this reception in Peking. There had always been several persons on hand to meet me wherever I went in China, including senior academic personages, and I knew that such receptions were organized for all Soviet specialists, whatever their degrees, qualifications, or merit. Then, too, I had expected Li Fu-teh, who I knew was now in Peking, to be there.

My puzzlement increased even further the next morning, when a tall, thin, bespectacled fellow entered my hotel room without even knocking and laconically informed me, "I am your interpreter."

A short time later, Liu Ta-kang came to see me from the Research Institute. We discussed plans of work for Peking and other cities. It was decided I would go to Mukden after the May Day celebrations.

"What's happened to Li Fu-teh?" I asked him. "Why hasn't he come to see me?"

"He is very, very busy," the professor said. "Every Academy establishment now has to keep its own pigs, and Fu-teh has been named foreman in charge of our Institute's pigsties. Forty members of the Institute are working under his orders."

I had always known of the versatility of Li Fu-teh's talents, but I had never suspected he was also an expert hog breeder and specialist in pigsty construction.

"And when will Su-fen come back from the countryside?" I inquired.

"She's been sent out for a whole year."

"How is that?" I said. "Surely you knew that I would bring my lectures with me, that they would have to be translated, and that I would spend time at your Institute? Surely you realized that Su-fen was the best person to help me with my lectures and to interpret for me during my office hours? It almost looks as if you deliberately packed off my friends just to keep them away from me."

Liu Ta-kang smiled sadly but remained silent. After a pause, he remarked: "Li Fu-teh will join you after the May Day celebrations. By then, he will have completed the pigsties. According to the pledges his work brigade made, they must be ready before May Day."

On April 30, however, Li called me and informed me in an alarmed voice that he had just been given a new assignment and would not be available during the holidays. He did not come to see me after the holidays either, and it was only about a week later that I accidentally bumped into him in the passage near the Institute library. He seemed embarrassed and depressed, and was extremely evasive when I asked him why he had not come to see me.

Later, I heard that Li Fu-teh was taken to task at one of those disciplinary meetings for deliberately hanging around in the hallway to meet "a Soviet specialist." I was told his defense was that his presence in the passage was purely accidental. It was clear that Li Fu-teh had received formal orders to keep away from me, and that this coincidental encounter had constituted a transgression. This is how Sino-Soviet friendship stood in the spring of 1960! It was now a crime for a Chinese interpreter to say hello to a Soviet specialist with whom he had worked for more than six months, a mistake grave enough to warrant "exposure" at a disciplinary meeting, along with heinous crimes of "revisionism" and "right-wing deviationism." This was an immense and extraordinary change from the former floods of praise for "our great Soviet ally" and the once enthusiastic odes sung to eternal friendship between the Chinese and Russian peoples.

I realized, of course, that all this was done on orders from above, and that my Chinese friends were not directly responsible for their evasions of me. I wondered how much any friendship could be worth under a totalitarian regime.

The superficial formalities of Sino-Soviet friendship, however, continued to be observed. During my first week in Peking, I received several invitations to attend ceremonies and banquets and, on April 28, I went to a huge demonstration of support for South Korea's eviction of President Syngman Rhee. The meeting was held in an open square about ten minutes from the hotel. I wanted to walk, but was obliged to go by car. We pulled up under the stands, where tea and lemonade were being served at refreshment stalls.

When we were seated in the stands, the meeting began with a speech by Peng Chen. He was followed by other VIPs, including the Soviet Ambassador, Chervonenko, who had recently replaced the scholar and philosopher Yudin in that post. All the speakers read prepared speeches, copies of which were distributed among the guests in the stands. At certain signals, the crowd emphasized with threatening roars selected passages, most of which were directed against "U.S. imperialism." (I was told later that a half million people had taken part.)

I also received an invitation to a formal May Day dinner for Soviet specialists at the Palace of the People's Representatives. There, I shared a table with Woo Yu-hsun, a vice-president of the Academy, Professor Liu Ta-kang, a fat Soviet geologist, his even fatter wife, and three other Chinese whom I did not know.

The President of the Academy, Kuo Mo-jo, walked around the tables, glass in hand and an amiable expression on his moon-like face. I am sure that the poor fellow had spent far more time in the last years at banquets and receptions than at research or his writing, or even at his office desk. Yet Kuo is a rather gifted writer and had been a distinguished historian, as far as I can judge from some of his work I have read in English translation. (I was given a present of several volumes of his works in the original Chinese, but when I left China, I left them behind with a pledge that I would return to that country and learn enough Chinese to read them.)

After an eight-course dinner with wines to match, the dining tables vanished as if by sleight of hand, and the floor was cleared for dancing. In other rooms, plays, concerts, and films were being offered to the public; in one, I saw a number of euphoric Soviet specialists, well in their cups, enjoying a contortionist performance given by young Chinese girls whose physical allure was as charming as their accomplishments were strange. Jealous Soviet wives strived in vain to drag their husbands away from the "shameful" show. In another room, a lotto game was organized for children of Soviet specialists.

The May Day celebrations went on for several days, ending with an extraordinary display of fireworks, which Soviet guests watched from a top platform, sipping tea and nibbling candies, while conjurors showed their tricks and dancers performed below them. The fireworks began as soon as it grew dark, and they were indeed a truly beautiful sight. At Moscow fireworks, the rockets streak up to form a haphazard pattern of red and yellow spheres, resembling clusters of children's balloons that have been allowed to fly away. In Peking, small brilliant spots first appear in the dark sky; these spots grow into beautiful arcs of large, bright stars—silver, green, orange, and red—rising higher and higher in graceful designs, then descending in other beautiful patterns and slowly fading away.

All week long, the constant theme at these festivities, these almost daily meetings, banquets, and receptions, had been the unalterable affection of the Chinese people for their "older Soviet brother." But I had frequent occasion to face the ugly, everyday truth behind these lofty statements in the person of my new interpreter. This young man had only recently completed a Russian course and was less proficient in it than my former interpreters had been, but what I found worse was the painful difference between his attitude (and manners) and theirs. He thought nothing of walking into my room without knocking, or of taking papers or a book from my desk without my permission, abruptly asking as he did so, "What book is this?" His diligence in searching out my effects was in vain, however, since my books were all "legitimate" and "on the level": every one but an English-Russian dictionary and a few technical books had been bought in China. Nevertheless, I resented his intrusion, and once, when I was particularly exasperated by his rudeness, I blurted at him that it was usual to knock before entering another person's room, and that before picking up something from another man's desk, it was essential to ask permission to do so.

After that, I tried to do without him as much as possible, for his chemical terminology was quite inadequate for my professional requirements, and, for my personal needs, I no longer needed an interpreter to guide me to the Institute and back to my hotel. But my attempts to be independent were the immediate cause of one unpleasant incident.

On May 3, I told the interpreter I would not need his services the next day and that he could have it off. I told him I was going to stay in my room until dinner and would be working on a lecture.

The following morning, I arose early and worked until the afternoon, when I decided to take a little break and go down to get some papers and magazines from a store on Wang Fu-tzin Street where they sold Russian-language publications. To reach it, I didn't even have to cross the street—the store was right around the corner from the hotel. Although the employees in the store spoke only Chinese, my scanty knowledge of the language was sufficient to explain to them what newspapers and magazines I wanted. (Incidentally, I saw in the window of the bookstore thirty or more journals published in China devoted to the physical sciences and engineering. Except for the titles, which were translated, they were all in Chinese. One of the more general scientific journals carried articles in European languages.)

The next morning, the interpreter came to my room and subjected me to a stiff cross-examination. Where had I gone? Why had I lied to him? etc.

"What's the matter?" I asked him. "I lived in Peking for six months in 1958 and I often went down to that store by myself."

"But now you are not supposed to leave your hotel alone even for a minute," he told me. "It is strictly forbidden. You should have told me you wished to go and I would have come with you."

That was the last straw. I told him off sharply, remarking that I considered his behavior very strange, beginning with his habit of entering my room without knocking and going through all his other habits that seemed to be a breach of good manners.

"Do you think I act that way because I like it?" he said. "I'm just carrying out orders. This is my first job as an interpreter. I know I am not very good. I was afraid I wouldn't be up to it and I even warned my superiors. And besides, I have TB." There were tears in the poor fellow's eyes.

Later, I heard from Soviet colleagues who had remained in China after I had left in 1958 that, beginning late in 1959, they had had to give up taking solitary strolls in town, and that from then on, they had to have interpreters with them even if they just stepped out of the front door of their hotel. If a Soviet citizen was seen walking in the streets alone, a car would drive up to him and he would be taken by unknown people either to where he was going or back to his hotel.

A few days later, Liu Tien-chang and I took off for Mukden, and I never saw that interpreter again. I assume he had faithfully and dutifully reported our last conversation to his superior, who may have decided that more diplomatic interpreters were needed to handle visiting Soviet specialists. I learned later that he had been sent to teach Russian in some school.

While Liu Tien-chang rushed from office to office, trying to locate nonexistent nickel-processing plants where we might find materials for our future work, I went round to libraries and bookstores seeking literature on the subject for the Kunming Institute. I now received an invitation to visit the spectrum-analysis laboratories of the Geological Institute in Peking. Spectrum analysis is used to determine the presence and proportion of the relatively small amounts of rare and precious metals contained in various ores. The method is basically fairly simple, and requires only small samples. The work carried out at the Kunming Institute depended to a great extent on this method, but the researchers there had not yet fully mastered it, since they lacked the proper apparatus. It was with some interest, then, that I went to see what the labs were like in Peking. It was immediately apparent: There wasn't a living soul in sight; the apparatus lay idle, some of it uncovered, some under dusty covers—clearly unused for a long time.

In one room, I found a group of young people sitting around a table talking.

"They are discussing political questions," I was told.

"But who are these people?"

"They are our laboratory staff."

I couldn't believe my ears. "But it is Monday today, not Saturday," I said. "Why are these people away from their labs and instruments in the middle of working hours?" I had become accustomed to the idea that Saturday, the last day of the working week in China's institutions of learning, should be devoted to "politics," but Monday! My hosts' reaction was a silent shrug. As they showed me around the labs, I realized that not only did they have no idea of how to use the spectrum-analysis apparatus, but they did not even understand the theory underlying that method or its importance. Yet how could it have been otherwise, when, at the very beginning of the week, they wasted their time on useless political chitchat? These were the vaunted "30,000 Chinese geologists, the pride and flower of Chinese science, China's largest learned army!" And this was in Peking, the country's capital; I wondered what could be the level of a geologist's training in a provincial town.

Peking had changed in many ways from what it had been in 1958, and the changes sometimes seemed to be contradictory.

In many places, tall new buildings had gone up. (Following the usual Soviet practice, the Chinese authorities erected large modern buildings on the main thoroughfares, in part to screen off miserable alleys and slums behind them.) A vast central square had been completed with a huge Palace of the People's Representatives and a spacious museum dedicated to the history of the Revolution. Inside, the Palace was beautifully decorated in luxurious good taste, and its auditorium and banquet halls were impressive in sheer size. From the outside, the effect was less happy: The building looked like a gigantic, squat barracks. Compared to it, the Museum building was graceful and airy. Many half-completed buildings that had been hidden under bamboo scaffolding when I left in 1958 were now finished—among them, Radio House—and new buildings were being constructed. Empty lots I had noticed driving to and from the Friendship Hotel were now the sites of large buildings. One plot had been turned into a park with pretty cottages and communal buildings scattered through it. This was reserved for visiting VIPs and was where Khrushchev stayed on his last visit to Peking. Possibly the rate of construction in 1960 was slower than it had been in 1957–58, but government offices, theaters, cinemas, and hotels were still rapidly rising all over the city.

The quality of building construction is higher in Peking than in Moscow, and, unlike Moscow, the collapse of walls in buildings under construction is not common. The water supply and plumbing in the new buildings also function satisfactorily. The Chinese superiority in these matters was well illustrated by the superiority of the Peking Chemistry Institute over its Moscow counterpart. Furthermore, Professor Liu told me the Institute was to get a new and yet larger building. I dare say my Moscow colleagues would have been only too happy to exchange their quarters for those their Chinese counterparts were about to discard. Living conditions in Peking had also changed during my two years' absence. In 1960, however, it was more difficult to get a good picture of what was going on, since the authorities were even more secretive and evasive than they had been in 1958; they felt that foreigners had no business nosing around in Chinese affairs, and now, Soviet citizens were very much foreigners too. Despite this, certain information could be obtained. It was well known that the monthly ration of meat per adult was only four ounces, and that the authorities invited people voluntarily to renounce these miserable portions so that they could be allotted to workers engaged in particularly strenuous physical labor. It was also common knowledge that flour and rice rations had been reduced and that, in some parts of the south, the rice ration was partly or entirely replaced by corn. Candy and gingerbread, sold freely in the Peking markets in 1958, could be purchased only in the lobbies of deluxe hotels. The easy availability of fruits and vegetables was now only a dream, and the allowances for cotton goods had been cut by almost 50 per cent.

In the streets, the people looked gloomy and preoccupied; the women's clothes were more uniform—and shabbier. Visiting foreigners, including the Soviet specialists, continued to enjoy the luxury hotels and still ate in exclusive restaurants where they ordered the best Chinese and European dishes, but they could hardly fail to notice the immense economic difficulties the Chinese were now facing.

On our way back to Kunming, Liu and I decided to stop over in Shanghai, where I ran into two other Soviet specialists, women from Moscow whom I had known in Russia. One had a doctor's degree that, according to persistent rumors among the Moscow chemists, she had received for praising the research done by the director at her institute. The other was a Candidate of Sciences and a conscientious rank-and-file metallographist. I was surprised to see the two of them in Shanghai, for I could not imagine of what possible use they could be to China. I knew that China had many specialists in metallography who were in no way less qualified than the second, for instance, for I had met them myself. On the other hand, they could not have come to China just to have a good time—although that, in the final analysis, was just what they were doing. On top of it all, they were both making good money as they went along, with China picking up the tab in accordance with the Sino-Soviet agreement.

My conferences and consultations at the Shanghai electrolytic plant took up all of two days. In all, I was impressed with the engineers' performance, and with the operation of the electrolytic section of the factory, where hundreds of tons of mixed and impure metal were quickly, efficiently, and *silently* refined.

There was time during our short stay, however, to get at least a glimpse of the city itself and of developments in it. Outwardly, Shanghai had not much changed since 1958, except for the disappearance of the fruit and vegetable stalls in the streets. We did, though, become acquainted with one radically new aspect of

Shanghai's urban life. Some time previously, the Chinese government had decided to tackle the problem of Shanghai's tremendous growth, of the increase in size of a city that was the largest in China and one of the five largest in the world. Their plan was to build several "satellite towns" around Shanghai in order to relieve the congestion in the center and the endless spread of suburbs on the outskirts. I visited one of these "satellite towns," the only one then completed, I believe.

As we drove from the center of the city through the suburbs, the houses became smaller and smaller until there were only vast, bleak stretches of tiny one-story cottages. Fields and vegetable patches began to appear and now and then a few clumps of trees. There seemed to be not a single patch of uncultivated land. Finally, after a drive of 25 miles or so, we came to the "satellite town."

This newly created city, planned to receive a population of fifty thousand, seemed quite pleasant and well thought out to me. The new houses were laid out in neat rows separated by attractive gardens and broad streets. A department store and hotel had already been constructed, and I also noticed two factories that had been built on the banks of the river not far from the town. Most of the future population, however, would work in Shanghai, commuting by train.

The system of satellite towns has aroused great interest among urban planners all over the world. I know that in the U.S.S.R., there has long been talk of building them, but, as far as I know, the first of them has yet to appear.

Liu and I stayed in Shanghai for only a few days, and then continued on to Kunming. We spent a short forty-eight hours in Hangchow on the way home, and there I met a Bulgarian "specialist in the field of philosophy." The Bulgarian and I spent several hours together, and I was fascinated by his recounting of his experiences. We dined together alone at one table, so we spoke quite frankly. (Like many Bulgarian intellectuals, he spoke Russian very well.)

He had been assigned to the Peking Philosophy Institute—which, like the Chemistry Institute there, is under the jurisdiction of the Chinese Academy of Sciences—and he told me he had been greatly surprised by what he had seen and heard there.

The Philosophy Institute was not interested in philosophy per se—i.e., in studying the theories and methods of knowledge. On the contrary, one of the major "philosophical problems" studied at the Institute was "the effect of the hour-wage base on labor productivity in agriculture"; another, the "People's communes: credits and debits." I am a mere layman in these matters, but I felt as strongly as the Bulgarian philosopher did that these were not exactly philosophical subjects. Yet, if a Chinese philosopher had dared to express such an unorthodox opinion, he would have been denounced immediately for his non-Communist or even anti-Communist outlook.

The Bulgarian philosopher had come to China with a "cultural delegation" of scientists, scholars, writers, and artists who were traveling all over the country studying the work of their Chinese counterparts. As a rule, the expenses of such cultural touring groups, in China or in other countries of the Communist bloc, are paid by their own government. They must not be confused with the groups of tourists who pay for their own trips. But travel abroad is a luxury few people in the Communist bloc can indulge in, even if it is only visiting another country within the bloc. Trade unions and certain other organizations therefore are awarded a few package-tour permits now and then, for a lucky one or two out of every thousand members. Those who wish to go abroad must make an official request and the most "worthy" —i.e., the most reliable from the regime's point of view, or, more precisely, from the point of view of the secret police—are selected. In 1960, it was rather more difficult to be accepted into a tourist group going to China than into one going to any other Communist country.

There existed yet another form of tourism, reserved for scientists and scholars in academic establishments who visit a country to attend a congress or conference, after which they go on an organized tour. In this case, the individual scholar must bear his own expenses. It was under this system that I took part in a trip to India in 1959, and it was how I arrived in Canada in 1961. But, as far as I know, no international conferences or congresses have been held in China since 1949. The Chinese government even insisted that the Moscow Institute of Chinese Studies be closed, probably fearing that it might probe too deeply into the social, economic, and intellectual conditions of their country. Later, the Chinese refused to send a representative to the International Congress of Orientalists held in Moscow, August 9–16, 1960. Actually, this decision was understandable, since the congress was held at the time of the mass departure of Soviet specialists from China. Of course, no Chinese could have come on his own, since no Chinese citizen is ever allowed out of his country for private purposes.

CHAPTER TWELVE

My Last Month in Kunming

When I had arrived in Peking in March, 1960, I had told Professor Liu and the officials of the Chinese Academy of Sciences that I had been sent to China for three months, but that they could have my services for another seven if they made a special request for them. Just before I left for Kunming, a certain Comrade P., who, unlike the usual type of Soviet official, was a friendly and well-meaning man, questioned me at length about my work and asked me for my schedule. (He then gave me a free theater ticket, the only free ticket I had ever received from Soviet hands while in China.)

Since June 16 was the expiration date of my three-month leave of absence, I telephoned at about that time from Kunming to Peking. When I heard Comrade P.'s deep voice in the receiver, I asked him about the permission to extend my leave. "Don't worry," he told me in a distinct voice, "stay on until December. The Chinese have requested an extension, and it has been granted."

A week later, the director of the Kunming Institute returned from Peking where he had attended a conference at the Academy and confirmed this news. And so I went on with my work.

Then, on July 16, Tan came to my office. His usually smiling face wore a preoccupied expression.

"I have sad news for you," he said, filling my glass with tea from a thermos bottle, "and sad news for us. I have just received a telegram from the Chinese Academy. You are wanted in the Soviet Union right away. They need you urgently."

What was going on? I knew well that it was right in the middle of the "dead season" in the Soviet Academy, and that not a research scientist was to be found in all of Moscow until September, even if you hunted for him with a candle. Perhaps the Chinese had not asked to have my contract extended? Yet nothing untoward had happened in the past months, and I had received my regular paycheck without comments. What a shame, I thought—just when work at the Institute had started to go full blast. It would be a crime to interrupt it at this point.

So Tan and I decided to send a telegram to the Chinese Academy to say that my departure had been delayed. In the meantime, I booked a phone call to Peking for the next day. This time, a female voice answered my call:

"Comrade P. isn't here. This is his secretary."

I explained my business to her.

"You must talk to Comrade S. about it," she said. "But he won't be here until July 20."

When I got my connection on that day, an unpleasant male voice introduced itself as Comrade S, informed me impatiently that I was being summoned by the Soviet government, that I was urgently needed at home, and that I had better get on the next plane for Peking.

I pointed out that I had to finish my work and that the Chinese Academy had especially requested that I be allowed to stay on, but this had no effect whatever. Comrade S. told me rather rudely that he could not discuss these matters further on the telephone and that there could be no question of delaying my departure even for one day.

The next day, I learned that the Chinese Academy's request to allow me to stay on, if only for two or three weeks, had been rejected by the Soviet authorities in Peking.

On July 23, Comrade S. called me on the phone and ordered me to leave without fail on July 24. At the same time, Tan received instructions from the Chinese Academy not to delay my departure any longer.

I decided to ignore Comrade S. and his orders: I could not leave in twenty-four hours. I had not completed my work and I still had two lectures to give, without which my associates would be unable to continue on their own. At any rate, there was no plane leaving Kunming for Peking on July 24 or 25, and all the seats had been booked on the July 26 flight. I got a ticket for a flight on July 28.

I told my troubles to two fellow Soviet specialists with whom I was having dinner one night. One of them told me he had heard of a Soviet citizen being ordered to return home within twenty-four hours simply because his passport happened to have expired.

"That's not the case with me," I told him. "My passport is valid until the end of the year, and my Chinese visa has been extended until November." But, a few days later, I learned that these two men had also been summoned home: One had had to leave for Peking at once, the other within the week.

Then, a rumor began to circulate that all Soviet specialists working in Kunming or in Yünnan Province had been ordered to prepare to return home without regard to the expiration date of their contracts.

I spent July 25 and 26 lecturing to my Chinese assistants on the theory underlying our work. On July 26, a photographer came and took a group picture of the entire staff of the Institute. I lined up for the photograph with Professor Tan on my right and, on my left, the "tall girl"—who had been putting in an appearance in the lab lately, perhaps because she had sensed my disapproval of her laziness.

In the evening, when I was preparing to leave the Institute, I was presented with the developed photograph and two beautiful china vases, which had been made in Kunming under Professor Chou Jen's direction. I did not wish to deprive my friends of these beautiful things and tried to refuse the gifts. They seemed slightly offended, and I told them again that I gratefully accepted the present but that I would leave them at the Institute in the safe-keeping of the director, as a pledge that I should return to Kunming. And so it was done. As I recall the incident now, I have a feeling of great satisfaction that those graceful vases remained with my Chinese friends instead of being seized by the Soviet security agents who ransacked my room and belongings in Moscow when they learned I had decided not to return to the Soviet Union—as they usually do on such occasions.

On July 27, the eve of my departure from Kunming, Min-pao told me that Professor Tan wanted me to come to the Institute in the evening. I thought it was for some last-minute consultation. When I arrived, Professor Tan, Che, and Liu Tien-chang led me to the room where I usually read my lectures. We entered the room and I discovered to my pleasure and surprise a group of Institute members gathered there for a farewell party. Tan gave a signal and the entertainment began.

It soon became apparent that every one of the twenty or twenty-five persons gathered at the Institute that evening had some special talent: Some played a musical instrument, others sang or danced. A shy analytical chemist turned out to be a fine violinist; the young woman lab attendant who prepared minute gold and silver specimens surprised me by the quality of her singing voice; the "tall girl" whirled spectacularly in a wild dance. But the most amusing performance was Che's. He sang passages from various classical Chineses operas in an incredible falsetto, making grotesque grimaces and faces; the whole audience roared their appreciation and shook with throaty Chinese laughter. After each number, I would go over to the performer and reward him or her with fruits or sweets, while the audience applauded again. The general mood was so enthusiastic, that to everyone's surprise, Tan's silent deputy, the man whom I had never heard speak during the entire four months I had been in Kunming, suddenly arose and sang, in a small but pleasant voice, a song that had been popular among the guerrilla fighters during the Long March.

In such an atmosphere of warm friendship, it was virtually impossible for me to turn down my friends' insistent demands that I too perform. This put me in a rather difficult spot, for while I have a fairly musical ear and know many Russian and Ukrainian songs, I have absolutely no singing voice, and even have difficulty with my lectures! But I did not want to offend them, so I decided to plunge ahead. I began with a sad Ukrainian song and then I sang one gay one, "Handsome Simon," which I had known since my childhood. The translation of that song into Chinese provoked a merry outburst of laughter!

That last evening in Kunming was undoubtedly the best gift my Chinese colleagues at the Institute could possibly have given me, and I appreciated it so much the more in that it was made while official Sino-Soviet relations were deteriorating—something that my Chinese friends must have realized more acutely than I, given their dutiful attendance at required political meetings. On that evening, though, the lecture hall at the Institute was filled, not with Russians or Chinese, but with human beings fraternally united by their common work; the feeling of friendship was not imposed by political decree, but was based on warm, human solidarity.

The next morning, some of the Institute members came to see me off at the airfield. It was a sad moment for me when, together with my traveling companion Liu Tien-chang, I left green Kunming forever.

CHAPTER THIRTEEN

My Last Weeks in China: Fighting for Time

In Peking, word of the mass departure of the Soviet specialists had spread, and we were paradoxically treated with greater consideration and cordiality than usual, for the Chinese had been instructed that they need no longer restrain their warm feelings toward their Soviet colleagues. No sooner had I stepped off the plane than I was surrounded by all my old friends and colleagues who had come to meet us: Professor Liu Ta-kang, Madame Lu Chen-yi, the gloomy Hua, and—I was glad to see—Li Fu-teh, the latter now wearing a well-cut beige jacket of good quality. But the man whose appearance surprised me most was Wang Tao, head of the Foreign Section of the Academy of Sciences.

The group of us headed for the airport restaurant, where we found ourselves the only patrons. When coffee had been served, Professor Liu turned to me and asked, "Which hotel would you prefer to stay in this time? Would you like to go to the Hotel Peking? Or perhaps you'd prefer the Friendship Hotel?"

"I'd like to go to some hotel where my Chinese friends can visit me at any time," I said, "where they would not need a special pass."

Liu went into a huddle with his Chinese companions.

"All right," he said after a while. "There is such a place. It would be the Chiang Men Hotel. I am sure you'll be quite comfortable there."

I agreed, and we drove to the Chiang Men Hotel.

That evening, I went for a walk with Li Fu-teh. I saw that people were lying out in the squares and even on the sidewalks, most of them with a piece of sacking under them and using their rolled-up shirts as pillows. I suppose it was too hot and stifling inside their houses.

I never had had any reason to complain of a lack of consideration on the part of my Chinese friends, the only exception being the cool reception I was given when I arrived in Peking in April, 1960, which, I am sure, had been determined by the official cooling-off between China and the Soviet Union. Now, however, I was treated like a spoiled child: Each morning, a servant brought me fruit for breakfast in my room. I had not been well, however, and the day after my arrival, I was taken to the Hospital of Sino-Soviet Friendship, where an attentive, elderly Chinese doctor prescribed some medicine for me that was thereafter brought to me fresh every morning in my hotel room; thanks to it, I felt well during all those last days in China, despite my strenuous exertions.

I went immediately to the Soviet Embassy and Consulate of course, but, just as before, the person I had to see was not there. I finally managed to trace the Comrade S. whom I had telephoned from Kunming.

At first, Comrade S. told me that my permission to stay in China had not been extended. But then he simply informed me that I was not a special case, that all Soviet advisers and technicians were being recalled, and that I must be on my way home no later than August 4 or 5.

I told him I could not possibly leave so soon and that it would take me at least three weeks to complete my work in Peking.

"The Chinese authorities," I added emphatically, "are doing everything in their power to get permission for me to stay."

"They won't get anywhere," Comrade S. said drily. "Every Soviet specialist is needed at home, for we have an urgent plan to fulfill too. The Soviet government has added two additional trains a week to the Peking-Moscow line, and we have received instructions from the Central Committee and from the Council of Ministers to complete the evacuation of all Soviet specialists from China before the end of August. There are about fifteen hundred here still. Counting their families, that makes more than four thousand people to transport. Only the Embassy officials, and a few economic attachés who will finish up the accounting, will stay." He continued to try to convince me that the sooner I left, the better it would be for all concerned. But I held stubbornly to my position.

Aside from the fact that I was in no hurry to get back to Moscow and that a journey from China to Russia seemed then like moving from a bright Celestial Empire to a gloomy, underground world, there was another, more important consideration that made me want to stay. Having observed the cheerless state of Chinese science and having realized that the development of science and research were the keys to the future of the Chinese people, I had no doubt in my mind that the soundest thing I could do would be to devote the years left to me to the service of Chinese science. I felt that I could be at least as useful in China as in the Soviet Union, but I could not ignore the order of the Soviet authorities. I decided, therefore, to prepare a comprehensive report on the state of Chinese science and on ways to improve it, in which I would explain clearly and bluntly what I thought, in the light of my thirty-five years' experience.

I had started to jot down notes for the report when I was still in Kunming, but it needed at least another two weeks of strenuous work. In Peking, however, I had to devote most of my time to lectures and consultations, not to mention those unpleasant visits to Soviet officials. The latter were disagreeable, but I was willing to do whatever was necessary to drag out my stay in Peking until I had finished the report.

Naturally, I never mentioned my plans to any Soviet citizen, for what I did in that report went beyond the directives I had received from the Soviet authorities when I left for China, and although I was trying to render service to a "socialist" country that was still officially considered friendly, my efforts could have been considered treasonable. On top of that, since I intended to give a truthful appraisal of Soviet assistance to Chinese science and pass judgment on my Soviet colleagues' work—a most unflattering judgment and appraisal indeed—one can easily imagine what would have happened if the Soviet authorities had found out about the report.

I was certain that the Chinese would not betray me, especially since it would not have been in their interest to do so. I decided that even if there were a serious risk of Moscow finding out about the report at some later date, it would not stop me anyway: I was prepared to risk my life for it. I considered that report as the culmination of my work for China, something that would help Chinese science more than anything else I had done there (except, perhaps, my Po Hai plan). I knew from experience that the Chinese would be discreet, for in 1958 I had left them two little reports—also above and beyond my official duties—one about how to organize research on precious metals and another on research in inorganic chemistry. As to my paper on the utilization of the Gulf of Po Hai, which appeared in a special collection of papers by Soviet specialists in China, Moscow paid no special attention to it, probably because it was published in Chinese.

My conversation with Comrade S. was inconclusive, and he sent me on to see an economic attaché.

I found two men, actually, and explained my case to them. The older of the two seemed familiar to me: He reminded me of Comrade K., the secretary of my precinct Party committee in Moscow during the purges in the 1930's, when I, like so many others, was the victim of persecution. When the man spoke, his voice seemed to confirm my suspicion.

He told me abruptly that I must leave Peking at the earliest possible moment, and cited again the orders from the Soviet authorities.

"But I still have three weeks to go until August 31, and if I cannot stay here until the end of the month, I would like to stay at least until August 16. I have even been paid through that date!"

He answered rudely, to the effect that there was no point in discussing government orders further. At that, I lost my temper.

"I realize you've received orders," I said, "but I also realize that you haven't bothered to give much thought to what is the best and most reasonable way of carrying them out. We have been working here in China with real, live people, and we have tried to do our utmost to strengthen our friendship with them and to be as useful as we could. But you seem to consider us just as cattle—you want to load us on a train, lock us in, and send us back to Russia. We Soviet scientists and engineers who came to work in China are not real people to you, not even cattle, but rather a pile of firewood you can toss into a railroad car and send off in any direction any moment you feel like it."

The two men stared at me with their eyes fairly popping. I

got up and walked out of the room, slamming the door behind me. Again I was leaving without having reached an agreement. I headed for the Embassy.

In the lobby, I told the receptionist that I wanted to see the Ambassador in connection with the work of a Soviet specialist in China. The man informed me that the Ambassador was out of town and suggested that I see the senior economic attaché, Comrade M., instead. After a brief conversation on an intercom, he turned to me again.

"I think it would be best if you came back in a couple of days," he said, "for it seems that Comrade M. is out of town too."

On Tuesday, August 2, a young Chinese came to see me, a representative of Intourist, and he brought me a ticket for the Peking-Moscow train leaving on Monday, August 8. I refused to accept the ticket, although the fellow kept insisting that he had been especially instructed by Comrade S. to hand it to me. Nevertheless, I was firm and the young man finally departed. For a few days more, I kept haggling with various Soviet officials, as a result of which the date of my departure was set forward to August 13.

(It was only after my return to Moscow that I was informed confidentially of a secret order issued by the Soviet Academy of Sciences that mentioned the disciplinary measures which had been taken against two persons, one of whom had "arbitrarily" delayed his departure from China, while the other, even more wickedly, had overstayed his time in a "capitalist" country by twenty-four hours. The same order also listed cases of misbehavior while abroad of personnel in the employment of the Academy, although not scientists—most of which had resulted from intoxication.)

During these last two weeks, I went to the Research Institute every morning to hold consultations on certain topics, and I also read a lecture on the proper utilization of literature on chemistry.

Every evening, I worked hard at my report—which involved spending a good deal of time in the Peking municipal library and the natural-sciences library of the Academy of Sciences. This report quite simply began with a query and my own answer to it, "Why is it that, despite the inherent ability of the Chinese people for scientific work, and despite the Party and government declarations of full support for scientific endeavors, Chinese science finds itself in such a lamentable state?" In answer, I enumerated the obstacles to scientific work in China that I have mentioned earlier in this book. I questioned the qualifications of some of the Soviet scientists who had been sent to China as advisers, for of the sixteen specialists I knew who had worked in China, at least half had proved to be obviously less qualified than many Chinese specialists in the same fields; for three or four others, it would have been possible to find Chinese substitutes; and only the last four or five could have rendered uniquely useful services to China if given the opportunity. I suggested that the Chinese authorities were wrong to invite advisers almost exclusively from the Soviet Union, but should consider the possibility of making some sort of agreement with England, France, West Germany, Canada, Holland, and the Scandinavian countries. I particularly emphasized the exceptional role English scientists play in world science. I mentioned the nations with which China had diplomatic or commercial relations, but also the major role the U.S. had had in training Chinese scientists, and suggested that Chinese students should be sent not only to the Soviet Union. Lastly, I mentioned certain measures I thought could improve the situation, and suggested an outline for research in chemistry for the next few years.

On the morning of Friday, August 5, Professor Liu Ta-kang and Madame Lu Chen-yi came to see me in my hotel.

"We should like to have a little chat with you," Professor Liu said. "Let's go to the salon and have a cup of tea together."

We left my room for the salon upstairs, chatting as we went about my consultations and the talks I was to give in the next few days. Then Liu lapsed into silence. Madame Lu Chen-yi turned to me and said, "We should like to acquaint you with the contents of two notes that have been exchanged by our two governments, and we have asked Shih-bing, who is our interpreter, to read them to you while you drink your tea."

The girl who sat facing me opened a folder, pulled out a folded paper, and began to read in Russian a Soviet note sent to the Chinese government in the middle of July, 1960. It contained all the sins by commission and omission imputed to the Chinese government. Here are the most important points:

1) The Chinese had not followed the technical advice of the Soviet specialists: They preferred to do things their own way, which was often exactly the opposite of what the Russians had advised them to do.

2) The Chinese were often scornful of the Soviet prescriptions: They crossed out passages, tore them up, and threw away the instructions given them.

3) The Chinese had created intolerable conditions and a painful psychological climate around the Soviet specialists: They spied on them, eavesdropped, searched their belongings, opened their mail, etc.

4) There had been instances of Soviet specialists being molested and even attacked. This proved that the specialists had not been adequately protected by the Chinese authorities.

5) All these things had happened despite the great assistance the Soviet government had given China. Therefore, the Soviet

government had decided to call back all Soviet advisers in China in the course of July and August—all engineers, technicians, skilled workers, scientists, and other Soviet citizens working in China.

When she had finished reading the document, Shih-bing stared at me with radiant, sad eyes. Liu pushed a cup of tea toward her. She took a couple of sips and fixed her eyes on me again.

"And now," Madame Lu Chen-yi said, "Shih-bing will read you the Chinese government's answer to that note."

The Chinese reply, dated about a week later than the Soviet document (I believe sometime between July 23 and 26), denied the Soviet accusations one by one. It pointed out that, while China greatly appreciated Soviet assistance and the help she received from Soviet advisers, she had paid for all services rendered. The Chinese had tremendous respect for the Soviet experts, the note went on, listened carefully to their advice, and were trying to make their stay in China as comfortable as possible. Therefore, the note concluded, to find fault with China's treatment of the Soviet advisers and to accuse them of spurning Soviet advice was "a strange and futile exercise, just like trying to catch the wind out in the fields." I remember this last expression, for it struck me, somehow.

Madame Lu Chen-yi asked:

"Well, what do you think of this?"

I told her that the contents of the notes took me completely by surprise, and that I would have to give the subject considerable thought before I could venture to voice an opinion on it. (I learned later that the Chinese authorities read these notes to *all* the Soviet advisers in China without exception, and it was this maneuver that had particularly provoked the Soviet officials' fury, for they, as usual, were trying to hide their little intrigues not only from foreigners but also from their own nationals.)

Now, cases of "spying" on Soviet specialists by Chinese authorities had indeed occurred, and many of us knew that our letters were opened. (Thus, if needed repairs in a hotel room—of a creaking door, a poorly fitted window-frame, etc.—were too long delayed, a Russian adviser, tired of making futile complaints to the management, would report in a letter to his relatives at home that "everything would be fine here if only they would do something about the squeaky door I've been complaining about for two weeks." A few days after the letter had been mailed, carpenters would arrive to fix the door.) Some Soviet technicians also complained about eavesdropping, and there was much talk of concealed microphones in our hotel rooms. But I must say here that the Soviet authorities themselves had tried to recruit Chinese agents on recommendations of the visiting specialists, or so I heard in conversations among Soviet citizens in China.

If I were to judge on my personal experience, I could not really say that my advice to the Chinese went unheeded. It is true that the work programs I suggested at the Institute in Peking were often changed, and some of the research topics I mentioned were occasionally thrown out. But then, I never considered myself an executive; I was an adviser—my job was to give an opinion whenever I felt competent to offer it, but it was up to the Chinese to use or disregard it. In any case, I certainly never saw the slightest suggestion of scorn on their part.

As to the safety of the Soviet specialists in China, it was true that incidents had taken place, although mostly in 1956–57, but the Chinese government did give effective protection to Soviet citizens and in outlying areas even provided armed escorts.

But even if we assume that the Soviet accusations against the Chinese were not merely partially, but fully, founded, the Soviet authorities could still have warned the Chinese first and given them a chance to mend their ways. In any case, I never heard a single Soviet adviser in China speak approvingly of the brutal Soviet note or of our sudden recall home. It was obvious that the recall had not been provoked by Soviet anger at the painful conditions under which we had lived in China, since for 99 per cent of us the life there was a good deal better than in the U.S.S.R. If any doubt had remained in my mind that our recall had been caused by anything other than the general deterioration of the political rapport between the two countries, it was completely eradicated after my visit to the Soviet Embassy and after I heard the report given there by Ambassador S. V. Chervonenko.

When I realized, after several unsuccessful requests to see the Ambassador, that I would never succeed in being received by him, I followed the receptionist's advice that I see Comrade M., the attaché, who had by now returned to town.

"I must stay at least until August 16," I told him, "since I've already been paid through that date."

M. heard me out and started to ask me a question. Suddenly, a younger man sitting in the same office blurted out, "Why do you try so hard to help them?" he asked impatiently. "Why do you need to hold more consultations with them? We've been giving them plenty, all this time, but what have we got to show for it? Not a damn thing! Let me tell you something: Once we asked them for some data on depths in the Gulf of Po Hai. Do you think they gave them to us? The hell they did! Or anything else we ask them for, such as what work has been done on the Amur? All they want is to get services from us, but they never do anything for us."

The young man, becoming more excited, darted from one corner of the room to the other, and his voice grew shriller and shriller. "In international policy," he cried, "the dirty tricks they play on us! I suppose they would like to be the leaders of the socialist bloc! Some leaders! They're starving and they'd like to lead!" He continued to pace the room, stopping now and then to exclaim, "Leaders! Some leaders, indeed!"

Comrade M. finally said, "All right, all right, but let's decide what to do about Professor Klochko."

"What is there to decide?" the young man asked. "He must take the train to Moscow. An order is an order. We have just three weeks left to pack off the remainder of the advisers and their families—that's about four thousand people—no easy matter, even with the two extra trains."

"All right, all right," Comrade M. said, interrupting him again. "Well, Professor, although it would be best if you'd leave right away, I'll let you stay till August 12 or 14. And, by the way, you must go and see the Party secretary, since you are a Party member, and remember that tomorrow afternoon the Ambassador will speak at a meeting of Soviet specialists, restricted to Party members."

I went to see the Party secretary and proposed to him that I pay my Party dues—3 per cent of my earnings during the past five months.

I poured out 80 yüan on the table, without argument, which apparently surprised the Party secretary, for visiting Soviet citizens usually preferred to keep their Chinese currency to make purchases with and to delay the settlement of their Party dues until they were back home and could pay in rubles.

At a quarter past three the next afternoon, Chervonenko, Soviet Ambassador to the People's Republic of China, a tall man of forty or so with horn-rimmed glasses, entered the Embassy auditorium and began to speak to the assembled Soviet advisers. He spoke, with a twenty-minute break, for about three hours, after which he answered questions from the audience. The afternoon was very hot: Both speaker and audience perspired heavily and kept wiping away the sweat with their handkerchiefs.

Officially, the Ambassador was giving this speech to fill us in on the decisions reached at the Plenary Session of the Central Committee of the C.P.S.U. in July, 1960. At that session, Frol Kozlov, a member of the Presidium of the Central Committee, had reported on the Third Congress of the Rumanian Workers' Party held in Bucharest in June, 1960, where a heated debate had occurred between Khrushchev and the Chinese delegate, Peng Chen.

As a rule, all Party organizations "study and ponder" the decisions reached at the Central Committee plenary sessions after these have been made public. Announcements about "closed plenary sessions" are made in "closed letters" to Party organizations and are discussed at "closed" Party meetings reserved for Party members, who are bound to secrecy and may not divulge what they hear to anyone who is not a member of the Party. But many things are said at plenary sessions that never reach the ears of the rank-and-file Party members.

But it was the Soviet government's unprecedented measure against its major Communist ally that had made this speech of Chervonenko's really necessary. Now, he had to explain the sudden recall of all the Soviet advisers and technicians working in China, without regard to the dates at which individual contracts were to expire. It is true that under Stalin a similar action had been taken against Yugoslavia, when, on March 18, 1948, all Soviet military specialists were summoned home, and the next day all the civilians. The Soviet press never mentioned a word about this recall until the final breach of all diplomatic relations with Yugoslavia.

In the present situation, the Soviet authorities seemed to follow a similar procedure: There was no hint in the Soviet newspapers about the mass recall of Soviet specialists from China, nor was there mention of notes exchanged between the two governments, of the existence of which we knew only through the courtesy of the Chinese authorities. Because those notes had come as a complete surprise even to the specialists who held Party cards, Ambassador Chervonenko had to explain the events that had led to the drafting of the Soviet note in the first place.

From the very beginning, Chervonenko tried to make it clear that although the Chinese were indeed guilty in many ways toward the Soviet specialists, that was not the only or even the major cause for the sharpness of the Soviet note. He then proceeded to enumerate the domestic and foreign Chinese policies that had provoked such great displeasure in the Soviet government and that had forced it to exert pressure on the Chinese by such measures as recalling technical aid.

In 1957, the campaign following Mao's slogan to "let a hundred flowers bloom, a hundred schools of thought contend" had been initiated in China. Moscow was taken aback by a slogan so incompatible with Marxism-Leninism, but let it pass without protests. Mao's thesis on the clash of interests between the rulers and the ruled was considered just as anti-Marxist, but the Ambassador did not explain why, actually, these two ideas were anti-Marxist.

Instead, at this point, he repeated the contents of the Soviet note, about the Chinese spying on Soviet specialists, throwing the blueprints away, ridiculing the advice offered, insulting Soviet citizens, etc. He remarked again that attempts had been made on the lives of Soviet technicians and their families, and that some murders and woundings had actually occurred in central China and Manchuria. Rejecting the Chinese reply as entirely unsatisfactory both in form and content, the Ambassador proceeded to denounce "Chinese attempts to spread subversive propaganda" among the Soviet advisers—such as reading the two notes and distributing the booklet *Long Live Leninism!* which contained articles criticizing the "general line" and policies of the Communist Party of the Soviet Union.

In Chinese internal affairs, the Ambassador paid most attention to the "people's agricultural communes." The Chinese, he asserted, had rushed into the "people's communes" without any of the technical, economic, or social prerequisites, refusing to take advantage of Soviet experience and learn from our mistakes. (This was the first time I heard a Soviet Party official describe Soviet agricultural policy of the 1930's and the intensive collectivization campaign as a mistake.) They had overlooked the fact, he pointed out, that, deprived of the profit motive, their peasants would cease to produce. In an overpopulated country like China, where masses of people can die in successive waves of famine, to form communes was to bring about the catastrophe with which China was now already threatened. It was clear that the Chinese authorities had failed to supply their people with food and, indeed, in organizing the communes, they had only further worsened the food shortage.

Chervonenko also denounced the Chinese for protesting against the founding of the Institute for Chinese Studies in the Soviet Union, an action that resulted in the Soviet authorities closing that establishment.

But the Ambassador's main target was the Sino-Soviet disagreements over international policy. He pointed out the inner contradictions in Mao's statements that, on the one hand, American imperialism was nothing but a "paper tiger," which was therefore hardly dangerous, but on the other hand, a nation so powerful that war against it was inevitable. (The Chinese continued to use that slogan about the inevitability of war at every international Communist conference.) He pointed out the folly of Chinese aggression against India, describing the latter as a "peace-loving democratic country that has only recently been freed from the colonial yoke." Chervonenko felt certain that, since the disputed area comprised nothing but a few deserted mountain passes, the argument could have been resolved in peaceful negotiation.

The Chinese were also responsible for the worsening relations between their country and Indonesia, another country recently liberated from colonial chains. "And for what reason?" Chervonenko exclaimed dramatically. "For the sake of a few petty merchants who, like foreign shopkeepers in many countries, were barred by a decree of Sukarno's from owning retail businesses in rural districts. It is as if we suddenly took it upon ourselves to protect the Russian White Guard refugees in China or Manchuria. Why can't the Chinese act as we did, when we told those people, 'Well, please yourselves. If you want to stay in China, become Chinese. If you don't, come back to the Soviet Union.' The Chinese merchants, who occupy a very strong economic position in Indonesia and yet insist on keeping their Chinese passports, retain a dual nationality while acting to the detriment of the native population."

The Chinese needlessly exacerbated their relations with Yugoslavia as well. Could they not follow the Soviet example, the Ambassador suggested, and, while denouncing Yugoslav revisionism, maintain reasonably normal contacts with that country? The pursuit of such a policy on the part of the Chinese government would have been of great help to the Soviet Union, whose position on many international problems coincided, after all, with the Yugoslav position.

On the other hand, he went on, China's excessive friendship with Albania, whose government had committed many grievous errors, indicated a policy there, as in many other parts of the world, that was the opposite of the Soviet line. China not only was trying to lure over to their side the countries on her border, such as North Korea and North Vietnam, but was also very busy proselytizing among the former African colonies, claiming that she had played a major role in overthrowing Western colonialism there too. The Chinese government was constantly inviting African delegations to Peking, where they were received by

Mao himself. Seminars and special courses were organized for the African visitors, in which the Chinese political line was strongly advocated. The Chinese subjected visiting trade-union delegations, groups of touring women, etc., to the same sort of propaganda. And, at the Bucharest Party Congress earlier that summer, the Chinese delegate Peng Chen had argued heatedly against Comrade Khrushchev's positions, although he had later agreed to sign a joint declaration with him.

The Ambassador then dwelt on the activities of Chinese government agents in South America and in Southeast Asia and Africa, activities that were in overt opposition to Soviet policy and intended to establish the leadership of the Chinese Communist Party in the socialist bloc.

Chervonenko was especially violent in his denunciation of the behavior of the Chinese delegation at the conference of the World Federation of Trade Unions that had taken place in Peking at the beginning of June, 1960. On that occasion, the Chinese delegation not only criticized Soviet international policy, particularly disarmament policy, but even went so far as to propose an independent resolution, so that the Soviet delegation was forced to threaten to leave the conference. Although a compromise resolution was finally adopted, the Chinese constantly attempted to sway the more than fifty delegations to their views, especially the South American ones.

The Ambassador found fault with the Chinese on many other points, but the grievance underlying all of them was that China had ceased to be an obedient tool of Moscow's policy—and was thus doomed to lose her way among the left-wing dogmatic heresies that presented such a great danger not only to China but to the Communist movement in general. As if that were not enough, China, as she set out on her mad course, was trying to take upon herself the role of leader of the worldwide revolution, although, of course, she was not in the least qualified for that role, either by proficiency in Marxist theory or in revolutionary practice.

Therefore, Ambassador Chervonenko concluded, the Soviet Union was forced to recall its technical assistance and to give the Chinese government the opportunity to ponder its actions and perhaps to mend its ways.

The first question that occurred to me was, who exactly was responsible for the recall? The most likely official answer would be the usual vague one of "the Soviet people," despite the obvious objection that the Soviet public had not even been informed of the matter. Was the Communist Party responsible then? No, since Party members were informed of the decision only *ex post facto*. The Central Committee of the Party? Hardly. I could not believe that the majority of them could be so stupid as to pass of their own free will a measure so harmful to the interests of the Soviet Union. Indeed, I have never met anyone, either in Russia or China, who tried to justify even in part the recall of the Soviet specialists. Just the opposite, in fact—from leading scientist to rank-and-file lab attendant, everyone emphatically disapproved of it or at least pretended to do so in my presence.

The second question that occurred to me was, what will become of the much vaunted Sino-Soviet friendship, described as "high as mountains, deep as oceans"?

Still, leaving aside the great many contradictory and contrived doctrinal statements that Chervonenko had made, he nevertheless had revealed a great many interesting things to us.

As for the Chinese government and the Chinese Academy, however, although they had been aware of the Soviet government's intention of recalling its specialists, the news was a real shock, as was clear from the statements made at a farewell dinner given to the departing specialists early in August. I had the impression that no one, not even the Foreign Minister, Chen Yi, who spoke at that dinner, could make any sense of the Soviet move. (And the Chinese realized full well that many of the Soviet advisers in China were nonplussed and disgusted by the sudden order to return home.)

This farewell dinner, held in the main hall of the Palace of People's Representatives, was attended by about four hundred guests, Soviet and Chinese. When the guests had taken their places, it was announced that Foreign Minister Chen Yi wished to address us.

The Minister spoke in a slow and solemn voice, thanking the Soviet advisers for their immense services to his country and wishing us good health and successful work when we returned home. He never mentioned the reason for our sudden departure.

Chervonenko then took his turn, to speak of the 6 billion rubles the Soviet Union had given China and the 10,000 Soviet specialists who had worked during the past ten years, helping China to build up her economy. A Soviet delegate followed with a short address whose general message was, "We've done so much for you, and you are not content?"

After the dinner and all the speeches, various entertainments were offered to the guests—a circus, films, dancing, and so on. But the guests' faces revealed a more than usual tension.

The next day, Professor Liu Ta-kang and Madame Lu Chen-yi invited me to come for a walk in the park. Both seemed depressed by the recent turn of events, and they asked me whether there was anything they could do to keep me in China a little longer. I assured them there was nothing they could do, and that if it had been up to me, I would have liked nothing better than to work there until my contract expired and to return to China for any length of time in the future, provided my government allowed me to come.

My last days in China were completely filled. Every extra moment between running from one Soviet official to the next, I devoted to consultations and to work on my report on Chinese science. I felt immensely energetic, and, by the end of the second week of August, my 10,000-word report was ready.

The Friendship Hotel was now deserted, and the school stood empty and desolate. By the beginning of September, 1960, not one single Russian remained out of a former population of hundreds. Thus an island of plenty disappeared in Peking's ocean of hunger and misery.

On the eve of my departure, the Institute and Academy organized a small dinner party in my honor in a little restaurant somewhere in midtown Peking. Secretary Tuh and all the others made warm, simple speeches without the usual high-sounding phrases. I thanked my hosts for their generosity and said that, although I had had great admiration and respect for the great Chinese people before coming to China, now, after a whole year among them, I had become deeply attached to that hardworking, wise, and artistic people. The happiness and welfare of the Chinese people was indispensable to the happiness and welfare of all mankind, and I viewed my modest services to the Chinese people as a service to humanity as a whole—the happiest lot that can befall a man. I assured my hosts that I would be ready to serve Chinese science to the fullest measure of my limited knowledge, but that I was uncertain that I would be able to return to them, since both changing circumstances and my advanced years made that eventuality seem unlikely.

Before I left, though, I told them, I wanted to make a small present to Chinese science, represented here by my Chinese friends. I wanted to give them a little report, an essay I had prepared on the state of natural sciences and technology in China today, with the main emphasis on physics and chemistry, in which I had been bold enough to make a few suggestions as to ways of improving the situation. It was probable that my essay contained error, but I hoped my friends would realize that I had not had the necessary time to check all my statements thoroughly. I could guarantee one thing: I had written exactly what I thought was right, without bias, without catering to anyone's opinions, whether my own or my potential readers'. Possibly, much of the report would not be to their liking, but I could say in all honesty that I had tried to put into it all my scientific training and my organizational experience, and that my preparation of it had been motivated by a feeling of love and respect for the Chinese people.

Having said that, I handed my report to Secretary Tuh.

The day of my departure, August 13, arrived. My train was to leave at 2 P.M. At eleven in the morning, Madame Lu Chen-yi called at my hotel to invite me to a "modest lunch." I was not hungry and declined her invitation, only later realizing that I had offended her.

A dozen or so people came to see me off at the station, including Wang Tao, from the Academy, and, of course, Professor Liu Ta-kang and some of his younger colleagues. The platform was teeming with people, for a whole party of Soviet specialists was being seen off by groups of Chinese friends. There were flowers everywhere, and cameras clicked at every moment. When it was time to leave, Wang Tao embraced me in a bear hug, there were farewells all around, and I climbed aboard just as the train moved off. My heart weighed down with sadness, I watched my friends waving their last goodby—and thought of the bleak contrast with their warmth and goodness that awaited me in Moscow.

Around midnight, I stretched out on the bunk and dozed off. A while later, through my sleep, I heard the door open and a woman conductor appeared against the lighted background of the passageway. I had difficulty in understanding what she was trying to say, but soon I realized that someone was asking for me. I dressed hurriedly and went out.

It was one in the morning, and we had stopped at Mukden. Two men were waiting for me by the door of my carriage. The younger of the two spoke first.

"You are Professor Klochko, I presume? Let me introduce myself, I am secretary of the Mukden branch of the Chinese Academy of Sciences, and this gentleman is its vice-president." He picked up a wooden crate and disappeared with it inside the train. When he reappeared, he said, "Your friends who saw you off in Peking had prepared a box of apples for you as a farewell gift. But the man who was to deliver them to the station was delayed and missed the train. So your Peking friends sent us a telegram, and here are the apples for you on their behalf. You must excuse us for them, though, because Liaoning Province had bad floods this year. Many orchards were inundated, and the apples are not of the best quality."

After we had crossed the border and the wheels of our carriages had been changed to fit the wider Russian gauge, I fell asleep. In the morning, a bulky woman walked into my compartment. She wore the gray uniform of a customs official and asked to see my luggage. When she saw that I had only one suitcase and one bag, she seemed most surprised.

"How long did you work in China?" she asked me.

"Five months."

She became even more puzzled.

"Do you have any printed matter with you?"

"I have a 'teach-yourself Chinese' book," I said, opening my bag to show it.

"Anything else?"

"No, that's all."

She thanked me politely and left. I am sure she had in mind the famous issue of *Red Flag* entitled *Long Live Leninism!*. Earlier, in 1958, no one had ever asked me whether I was carrying any printed matter with me.

I met many other Soviet specialists on the train who had left China before their time had run out; there were also quite a few railroad men, and some men who worked near the border. From all of them, I heard interesting stories about life in China and the changes in Soviet-Chinese relations that had taken place in recent years. Some of them reminisced about their attempts to help the Chinese people they had found starving, sometimes in Peking itself. And some of them claimed they had known of the deterioration in Sino-Soviet relations for some time, and of the Chinese subterfuges toward Russia, but, in general, all of them had been on friendly terms with their Chinese hosts and co-workers.

Still, I was not happy at leaving China and going back to the Soviet Union. I had seen misery, hunger, ridiculous campaigns and drives, endless political meetings, and many other things both absurd and terrible, but as far as I was concerned, I had felt I was doing constructive work. I had not been blinded by the comforts of my life in China, or the kind attentions which, for the first time in my life, I encountered everywhere; I knew well that the Chinese people suffered difficulties and deprivations in their daily life. But nevertheless, it seemed to me that life would be better in China than in Moscow. In the Soviet Union, most of my time was doomed to be spent on the futile defense of my scientific positions against the ceaseless attacks of ignorant careerists and intriguers. But the main thing was that in China I had had the feeling that my work was needed and appreciated, and that I was free and safe from the MVD agents, such as those to be found in all the ranks of our Chemistry Institute in Moscow. That feeling of safety in itself was worth anything else!

I got back to Moscow on August 22, 1960. My colleagues at the Institute, slowly trickling back from their summer vacations, were shocked and amazed by our recall from China. No one approved of the move; some even went so far as to express some mild criticism, but, of course, people never dared to say exactly what they thought.

I presented a report at the Institute on my sojourn in China and on the work I had done there, but I made it as brief as possible—only sixteen pages, instead of the sixty I had given in 1958. And my oral discussion lasted scarcely twenty minutes.

Until the early summer of 1961, I continued to receive letters from China, some of which, carried over the border and only mailed in Moscow, even reached me without having been opened by the censors. From those uncensored letters, I learned that the food shortage in China had worsened even further.

Later, there was a rumor that I might be sent to China once more, but until my departure for Canada in August, 1961, I never heard of any Soviet specialist—or at least any employee of the Soviet Academy of Sciences—being sent to China.

I worked in Moscow for a month, until early in September, 1960, and then took my vacation. I returned to Moscow and worked steadily there until the summer of 1961. In February, 1961, I heard for the first time about a forthcoming international conference on pure and applied chemistry to be held in Montreal. I spared no effort to get to attend that meeting, in order to leave the Soviet Union once and for all.

And in this I was successful.

CONCLUSION

Observations on Modern China

There are two milestones on the path of development of world science: The first marks the transition from the oral transmission of accumulated knowledge to written records; the second, the addition of experimentation to mere observation. The first milestone was passed at different times by many societies in many countries, including China; the second, at more or less the same time, and only in Europe—that was about four centuries ago. Until this latter transition from simple observation to experimentation with improved instruments and apparatus led to the dramatic achievements of European science in the modern world, Chinese science had been among the most advanced in the world. Then, while Western science accomplished wonders in advanced techniques, experimentation, and discovery, Chinese science made little progress. Japan, where modern Western scientific methods had been applied in the last third of the nineteenth century, continued to advance to her present position as a highly industrialized country.

Still, China was not wholly impervious to modern accomplishments. She had had many isolated but genuine contacts with the West since the late seventeenth century, but Chinese science did not truly begin to modernize itself until the 1920's. Before the Chinese revolution of 1911, a true scholar in China was popularly considered to be one who more or less confined his studies to literary criticism, to philosophy, ethics, and the study of Confucian teachings. Scholars in these fields had looked down with scorn on those who spent their time in experimentation, medicine, engineering, etc., considering them on a level with the searcher for the "life-giving elixir" that would prolong the emperors' lives.

But after the 1911 revolution, which deposed the feudal regime of the Manchu dynasty, the Chinese government began to send thousands of young people to Western countries and Japan; it was these people who, upon their return home, laid the foundations of modern Chinese science and of new teaching methods.

Needless to say, China's exposure to Western science and education was badly slowed down and delayed by the poverty and backwardness of the country, which, in addition to everything else, was torn by internecine wars, subject to the whims of provincial war lords, devastated by the Japanese invasion and the civil war. Nevertheless, by 1949, when the Communists came to power, there had been considerable progress—due primarily to the several tens of thousands of young Chinese who studied in Europe and the United States during the 1930's; by the end of World War II, China had two or three hundred thousand persons with a university education, of whom about 1 per cent had had some experience in research. Some scientific periodicals began to appear. It seemed that, with the arrival of calmer times, progress in science would be considerably speeded up.

When the Communists took over the country in 1949, they announced that they viewed the natural sciences and engineering as matters of prime importance to the national economy and military defense. Instead of the two old academies, one single one was created. This was an optimistic time for Chinese science. The budget and staff of the Academy of Sciences grew apace, beginning about 1957, after the Chinese government engaged upon the Twelve-Year Plan for the Development of Science. (According to Peking figures, 7,000 persons worked under the aegis of the Academy of Sciences' various branches, out of a total of 32,000 researchers employed in China in 1959.) We can deduce from the few available statistics that China had about 4,500 men with advanced education in the sciences by 1960; roughly one half of these had received their training in the U.S.S.R.

The progress of Chinese science under the Communist regime was determined in the main by two considerations: Organizationally, the Chinese set-up was modeled on that of the Soviet Union; secondly, Party bureaucrats had only a very poor grasp of the special problems of developing Chinese science.

Following the Soviet example, the Chinese based their scientific research in specialized institutes rather than at the universities. This proved to be a great mistake, for there were simply not enough trained and educated technicians to make the system work. There were so few scientists that their efforts were hardly discernible, nor could they have much effect on the development of the national economy or the country's living standards. These scientists would have been more usefully employed in teaching, where they could have trained future technicians and researchers. In short, this relatively small number of trained scientists in China can be compared to a handful of rare seeds: A clever botanist will treat each seed with care, plant it carefully in a separate pot in the soil that suits it best, and look after it lovingly, doing his best to see that each plant should give as many new seeds as possible—hoping that one day in the future, the precious seeds can be sown over a wide area of land and yield a rich harvest. The most favorable conditions possible should have been created for every Chinese scientist, and his main task ought to have been the training of his pupils. Assuming that each scientist could have trained ten new men capable of taking over his research in ten years, the Chinese could have produced enough scientists of their own.

But instead of following this seemingly obvious course, the Chinese rulers built a great number of research institutes, spent enormous sums on equipping them, only to find out that they had no people with whom to staff them. In the first decade of their regime, the Chinese Communists had failed to create even a middle-echelon corps of scientists.

At present, therefore, Chinese higher-education institutions are in a lamentable state. The professors and instructors have time for neither teaching nor research nor, for that matter, advancing their own work. The neglect of research in educational institutions, too, was a consequence of China's blind copying of the Soviet system.

It should be added that the Soviet Union was partially responsible for China's error, for it was she that had oriented China toward a scientific structure based on her own, without taking into account that for the system to work, there must be sufficient scientific cadres of trained specialists to assure the progress of teaching and genuine research. (In the summer of 1961, the Soviet Academy of Sciences gave the same bad advice to North Vietnam: Instead of advising the Vietnamese to found a good university, some of whose students could engage in research on completion of their training, the Academy advised them to create a "scientific research committee." But the Academicians, some of whom had spent time in Vietnam in 1960, must have known that the North Vietnamese could not possibly have enough qualified scientists to engage in such a scheme.)

The Chinese to this day slavishly follow the Soviet course.

Instead of having a good university in each province, with a body of graduate students selected for training in teaching and research, they have set up in each province "provincial branches" of the Academy of Sciences, which consist entirely of bureaucrats. This reminds me very much of the Soviet Union, where some Soviet Republics with a population of one or two million have their own Academies of Science, although they have no university worthy of the name.

I might point out that at the time when the Sino-Soviet cultural-exchanges agreements were concluded, Soviet science had just emerged into a relatively tranquil period. For decades before 1955, a scholar or scientist had never headed the Scientific Service of the Central Committee of the C.P.S.U., and consequently the measures affecting research and researchers were very often incoherently planned and badly worked out. In addition, although it would be inexact to speak of a systematic persecution of scholars in Russia, the purges of the 1930's had struck the scientific community severely. For many years, any one with any culture or advanced education, even if acquired after the advent of Bolshevism, had become accustomed to the expectation that he might, at any moment, be arrested, shot, or sent to the Siberian concentration camps. Meanwhile, scientific work itself was prey to the changing directives of the Soviet government: At one moment, one would be allowed to concentrate on essential pure research; at another, it would be decreed that all science had to have practical application.

In any case, research in physics and chemistry was always encouraged—which explains to a large extent the Soviet advances in rocketry and nuclear power, advances that in the West are too often attributed either to mysterious miracles or to the contributions of German scientists.

It was certainly clear that Russia was well equipped to furnish technical and scientific aid to China in 1957. Without disrupting her own research and industrial work, she was fully able to send to China a considerable number of specialists, some of them highly qualified, others of debatable competence, as I shall point out later.

But when it is a question of organizing science in a country as large and complex as China, the amount of money and mere size of the venture is not the crucial factor. To acknowledge that scientific development is necessary is only a beginning: It still remains to take measures to further that development in practical, realistic ways. The Chinese government did not understand that, to apply modern scientific techniques to daily life, these methods and techniques must be founded on a solid foundation of careful basic research. Instead, they relegated research projects in the institutes and universities to the second priority, and paid not the slightest heed to the fact that in order to accomplish good work, years of preparation were necessary. They failed to realize a self-evident truth—namely, that scientific work is one of the most skilled forms of human endeavor, and demands, besides talent and ability, a long and thorough preparation. Michael Faraday said that in order to become a good experimentalist, a man must spend several decades in strenuous work. But, in China, the government believes that any man can engage in scientific research no matter whether he has had training or not.

In addition, the Chinese research institutes have no learned councils qualified to discuss new scientific developments, to further work programs, or to report on the work accomplished thus far. Only occasionally are scientific problems discussed at all— any discussion that is held is concerned mainly with general subjects, with reading and approving directives from the government and the Party.

Until 1950, Chinese scientific journals were published in English, but after that in Chinese. At first, the tables of contents were continued in European languages, but eventually even that feature disappeared. This is reminiscent of Stalin's last years in the Soviet Union, when it was considered almost criminal to refer too often in one's papers to foreign sources, and when it was also forbidden to publish the tables of contents in foreign languages.

But there are, of course, peculiar difficulties for Chinese scientists in this matter of languages. How, in their ideographic system, did Chinese chemists, for instance, go about naming the chemical elements? Now, before chemistry became an organized science, at least a dozen elements had received different names in every language—iron, copper, sulfur, lead, etc. But for all the remaining elements, whose discovery came only with the modern development of chemistry, the names have essentially the same sound in all languages. Yet, ruthenium, for instance, which is *rutenii* in Russian and *ruthénium* in French, becomes *lao* in Chinese! To make things even more difficult, *lao* has a good dozen other meanings as well. By the same token, try to guess whether a Chinese means his youngest sister, magnesium, or the United States of America when he speaks of *mei*.

The difficulty of the ideographic system has opened a great gap between the spoken and written languages, causing untold damage to Chinese literature and science. This gap became so unbearable that a movement for bringing written and oral Chinese closer together was initiated in 1917, headed by the well-known philosopher Hu Shih and by the sociologist Chen Tu-hsiu. Since then, foreign missionaries and sinologists, as well as Chinese scholars, have made repeated attempts to introduce a system of writing based on phonetics. Some proposed the Latin alphabet, others the Cyrillic, others an alphabet based on the Chinese ideograms. All these efforts were directed to a radical phonetization of the Chinese written language. The latest of these attempts, dating from February, 1958, was to introduce the Latin alphabet by law—a measure adopted on the advice of a study group that had worked on the question for several years. In Chou En-lai's speech on the matter, it is argued that, for the time being, the new alphabet is not meant to supersede the old ideograms, but is to be used as an auxiliary aid in the study of Chinese, in writing foreign words, in compiling dictionaries, in classification, and in cataloging. But the use of the Latin alphabet is still limited. It is used today really only by newspapers, magazines, and commercial enterprises—in headlines, titles, and advertisements. Lately, it has occasionally been used to explain the pronunciation of certain ideograms. At the same time, about 500 of the most frequently used ideograms were simplified so as to reduce the average number of strokes making up each one from about sixteen to eight.

The only serious argument put forth by the champions of the old Chinese system was its "unifying" role. Dialects throughout China vary so much that when a Cantonese gives a lecture in Peking, he needs the assistance of an interpreter. (In the Russian Far East, I once heard, two Chinese from different regions conducted a conversation in halting Russian.)

But, of course, ideograms have the same meaning throughout China, different though their pronunciation may be. And, despite the radical difference between the Chinese and Japanese languages, a literate Chinese can read "Japanese," although he may pronounce it in his own way.

The second argument against the introduction of the Latin alphabet is the difficulty of realizing such a project—for there are innumerable words in Chinese that are homonyms when spelled in Latin letters, but are clearly different when represented by ideograms.

Now while these arguments against the phonetization of the

Chinese written language are worthy of attention, although not wholly convincing, there are other arguments advanced against it that are ridiculous. Some contend, for instance, that doing away with the ideograms would result in a loss of the Chinese classical heritage. But in reality, it is, perhaps, just the opposite. As things are now, very few literate Chinese can read and understand the ancient Chinese books without special annotations. In introducing the phonetic alphabet and improving the structure of the literary language itself, the best works of Chinese literature could be transcribed and would become accessible to the masses of the Chinese people.

Another "patriotic" argument is that ideograms are an integral part of Chinese national life and must be maintained as such. But we all know that not all that is old is necessarily good. Finally, there is also the ridiculous argument that the disappearance of the ideograms will put an end to the old Chinese art of calligraphy. Those who argue along this line even oppose the simplification of the characters, calling it a "loss of artistic equilibrium." There seems to be no need to comment on such a childish assertion here.

Many of China's most forward-looking minds were in favor of the phonetization of the language, and the country's greatest twentieth-century writer, Lu Hsün, was an ardent advocate of Latinization, who wrote biting and sarcastic pieces about my colleagues the chemists, for not using Latin names and usual symbols for the elements, and for having invented new ideograms to represent them instead. If chemists could not learn the twenty-six letters of the Latin alphabet and use them to designate chemical elements, he said, their worth as scientists could not be great.

How will China overcome its language difficulties in the future? The use of a foreign language in science, English for instance, would be an acceptable solution. The *Journal of the Chinese Chemical Society* was published in English until 1949. The Chinese could also introduce the phonetic alphabet into all the branches of science and culture while preserving, for the time being, a parallel text of ideograms for those to whom such an abrupt transition to the Latin script would be too difficult.

To a considerable extent, the state of Chinese science today can be accounted for by Mao's understanding—or we should rather say misunderstanding—of the role of science in a modern country. It cannot be said, however, that the Chinese leaders are altogether unaware of the importance of science for the national economy or military capabilities of their country. Important sums of money have been allotted for the construction of research institutes, to keep large numbers of research workers on the payroll, to supply them with the necessary equipment and materials, to purchase specialized literature and apparatus abroad and, above all, to send, during the past ten years, at least 10,000 Chinese to complete their studies abroad—mostly in the countries of the Communist bloc, above all in the Soviet Union. But even these allocations for scientific development are minimal for so large a country. But that is not the main trouble. Recognition of the importance of science does not imply a grasp of the ways and means of science and research. Yet this is indispensable if science is to flourish and if the best use is to be made of its learning for the nation. It is precisely this point that the Chinese leaders have failed to understand. They do not see that basic, pure research is the cornerstone of all applied science. Instead, projects of pure science are mercilessly tossed out by the bureaucrats. This dooms Chinese applied science from the start, and forces it to imitate foreign prototypes and borrow alien ideas.

Another factor limiting the development of Chinese science is that it is so remarkably insular. There is no longer any contact with the developments of science in other countries, and this despite the fact that such exchange, contact, and flow of information is essential to scientific progress. The Communist Chinese are, moreover, still persuaded that a theory, even a scientific theory, is true, not if it has been verified and proven in experimentation, but when the person who repeats it commands authority.

In addition, both Party and government consider all scientists, especially those belonging to the older generation, as "class enemies" who can never be trusted. In taking this attitude, they forget that a person's "class" can change, and that it did change for scores of millions of people in China, not to mention the fact that a man's mental make-up is not exclusively determined by his class origin or his parents' wealth.

There are other difficulties impeding the development of Chinese science. Not the least of these is that the most gifted students in China seem automatically to be absorbed by the army, the police, and other organs of the regime's political control. The other side of this coin is, of course, that the Academy of Sciences must, at its universities, accept not only those students who are capable of and gifted in scientific work, but also those who have only received a rather mediocre general education. Lastly, there is the terrible secrecy that the Party imposes on all scientific research. Not only are contacts with the outside world cut off, but between different branches of China's scientific community and within one branch.

We may assume that if conditions for scientific work in China were better, many Chinese scientists now working abroad would have returned to their country. Although I must say I did not meet many scientists who were fanatical Communist ideologues, I am certain that all of them were loyal patriots. (This, by the way, was demonstrated during the Japanese occupation, when many Chinese scientists and students, braving danger and privation, escaped from the invaders into unoccupied provinces and devoted themselves to teaching and research under very difficult conditions.)

Ever since about 1957, the free world press has been discussing whether China will be able to produce its own nuclear weapons—with or without Soviet assistance. Various pronouncements by Chinese statesmen have been cited, and all sorts of prognostications have been made on how soon China will have an independent atomic capability and, in particular, when it will explode its first atomic bomb.

Serious students of conditions in China, on the other hand, have pointed out the difficulty of creating an atomic weapon in a technically undeveloped country, such as China still is today, despite its progress in industrialization. But even these serious students have made two errors: They have taken the assurances of Chinese statesmen at their face value; and they have not made proper allowance for the peculiarities of the Chinese set-up and the strange lines along which it has developed since 1949.

People in the free world tend too often to forget that every public statement made by a Communist leader aims above all at achieving the effect desired by the propaganda experts, and that they do not feel in the least restricted by the truth. This is especially true when the statement is aimed at foreign audiences. For the famous Communist theories of government and society, to which Mao also supposedly adheres, are nothing but myths. The only real source of these "theories" is the dictator; theory is simply what that dictator thinks, writes, or says. What difference does it make if his affirmations are in formal contradiction with earlier ones? What if he affirms today what was declared false yesterday, simply to prevail over his opponents? All who contradict him will be "revisionists" and "deviationists." The authenticity and solidity of the dictator's theory rests not on arguments but on the fear of the secret police: When the dictator dies, when the fear he inspires disappears, his heirs will liquidate all the former theories and proclaim their own as the only source of truth. Those who attempt to justify the policies of a dictator according to established theories are fooling themselves and wasting time. And we might well note that each Communist dictator reserves for himself the exclusive right to interpret the great masters of Marxist thought. Khrushchev and Mao, for example, therefore offer perfectly contradictory interpretations of Lenin.

Thus, the striving of the Chinese rulers, especially Mao Tsetung, to acquire military equipment, and above all nuclear weapons, is determined not so much by "ideological" considerations as by considerations of prestige: In their opinion, any first-class power must have the full array of weapons that would enable it to conduct a full-scale modern war. But Mao knows well that all his bellicose pronouncements do not change the facts: Without Russia's aid, China could not wage war, and the threats against the United States, the Seventh Fleet, Formosa, etc., are nothing but childish scarecrows. But it also goes without saying that the question would never arise of Khrushchev's handing Soviet nuclear weapons over directly to Mao. But, in addition, in 1963, when it became clear to everyone that the Sino-Soviet conflict was almost irreparably widening, talk about Soviet assistance to China's efforts to create a nuclear capability began to die out. Until then, because of the help the Soviets gave in building the atomic reactor near Peking, which began operations in 1958, many people thought that Soviet assistance would extend to include the military uses of nuclear energy. It is quite possible that, needing Mao's support in installing himself on the Kremlin throne, Khrushchev made certain promises to his Chinese colleague during Mao's visit to Moscow in November, 1957. But even during Khrushchev's mysterious short visit to Peking in July–August, 1958, he was already alarmed by the Chinese plans to bombard Quemoy and refused his assistance in producing a Chinese atomic bomb.

In 1958, while in Peking, I often met a particular Soviet specialist who was there to lecture on his special field in nuclear chemistry. In preparing his lectures, this Soviet expert used exclusively American publications, because at that time there still was no non-classified Soviet literature on the subject to speak of. He himself had only an M.A. in chemistry, and he had had very little research experience. All too often, the Soviet Union sent to China only middle-echelon specialists, especially when it came to matters of possible military application.

To build up an *independent* nuclear capability, either for peaceful or military use, any country needs to have the indispensable raw material—uranium and thorium ore, as well as other materials. On top of that, it must have a highly developed industry and a great number of well-trained scientists and technicians, and its government must be willing to allocate huge sums to the development of a nuclear capability.

China has the principal raw materials required; the branches of industry that are indispensable for the development of nuclear energy for military purposes could be sufficiently developed in ten to fifteen years if circumstances are favorable. But then, the development of a military nuclear industry demands huge capital investments of which China is not now capable, nor is she likely to be in the next ten years or so. But the main obstacle to China's development of her own nuclear weapon, and one which is not generally taken into account in the West, is the organization of Chinese science and the conditions of scientific work there.

The first prerequisite for the creation of an atomic industry in China is a complete reorganization of the entire system of national education, of the training of scientists and technicians, and of their working conditions. We may therefore conclude that it will be a long time before China joins the nuclear club, since, in any case, as long as Mao remains in power, any such changes are extremely unlikely, particularly when one considers that there was complete stagnation in Chinese science in 1958–60, from which the country only started to recover very slowly late in 1961.

At this point it may, of course, be objected that similar assessments were made of the Soviet ability to produce its own nuclear bomb, but that, in the end, the U.S.S.R. created a bomb only a few years after the U.S. But then, during the 1950's, the Soviet Union was nowhere near so far behind the United States in its scientific development as China is behind the Soviet Union today.

It can also be assumed that before China has an independent nuclear capability, Mao Tse-tung will have vanished from the political scene, and that his successors will find their hands too full of work at home to bother with mad foreign adventures. It is quite different, of course, when it comes to the peaceful use of atomic energy. It is to be hoped that Chinese efforts in that direction will be pursued—for the benefit of China's industrial power and of her general economic development, both of which are held back today by the unreasonable policies of her present rulers.

In conclusion, then, what is the actual situation in present-day China? Despite all the regime's efforts to disguise the truth, it becomes apparent that the facts are tragically simple: Chinese agriculture has never been in so terrible a condition, so disorganized and so incapable of furnishing food for the population; not only has industry not developed but its speed of production is slowing down; industry lacks electric power and basic raw materials; China's foreign trade has deteriorated and diminished. And all that Mao tries to do will not hide these truths.

Now, all Communist regimes go in for distortion of fact and mis-use of statistics, but it is probable that the record is held by the Chinese People's Republic. There was, for instance, the estimate of the 1958 crops. At first, it was declared that the year's grain harvest would be double the 1957 figure and reach 375 million tons. But in 1959, the Chinese regime had to acknowledge that the actual figure was only 250 million. Many authorities on China consider even that figure inflated by 15 or 20 per cent, but even if we assume it is fairly close to the truth, still, an error of 50 per cent in the estimate of a major product like grain makes the credibility of Chinese statistics questionable as a whole.

The deceptive techniques used by Communist governments— aimed at presenting something of poor quality as something excellent, passing off a small amount as a large one, pretending that something nonexistent exists—are augmented and aided by the tremendous amount of secrecy. Not only are matters concerning national defense and aspects of the national economy connected with it secret in China, but anything that touches on any official matter. Foreigners, including those from Communist-bloc countries, are allowed to know only what filters through to the foreign-language journals. Foreign tourists are given certain standard tours and shown only what their hosts think they ought to see. Contact with Chinese, observation of their everyday life, information about their diet, living standards, etc., are made considerably more difficult than they have been at any time in the Soviet Union. Even the sessions of the Chinese parody of a parliament, the National People's Congress—which once were open to the public—were declared closed in March, 1962.

But Communists and the advocates of free enterprise agree that statistics is a basic material for the development of economics as a science. The more advanced a country's economic life, the better organized its statistics. It would follow that statistics and accounting should be considered most important in Communist countries, whose governments attempt to plan the entire economy. One might have expected, therefore, that as soon as they took over the country, the Chinese Communists would have organized an irreproachable statistical apparatus. But in 1949, there were only a few trained statisticians, who had been working in various institutions of the defunct Chinese republic, in the entire country. At first, the Communists used them to take a census, which was completed in 1953, and which, with all its defects, is, after all, the first complete census ever made in China. But as time passed, statistics degenerated as a serious intellectual endeavor, for the trained specialists were gradually superseded by or subordinated to people whose sole qualification was their eagerness to please the Party bosses. After that, Chinese statistics lost all pretense to scientific accuracy and became an instrument of governmental propaganda. Now, industrial enterprises, agricultural communes, educational establishments, research institutes—all inflate the statistics of their achievements in order to "fulfill" and "over-fulfill" their plans. As these reports travel toward the political center, from village to town, to the provincial capitals, and finally to Peking, the data swell and swell for, obviously, in order to "over-fulfill" their own plans more impressively, the provincial administrators have a vested interest in further inflating the already inflated figures they receive from the villages. Hence the wild statistical extravaganza. During those endless Chinese production drives, too, various establishments and enterprises send altogether improbable figures concerning their vaunted achievements to the central authorities, since they are less afraid that their claims will be exposed sometimes in the future than they are that their superiors will be immediately angry with any "failure." This seems to be the only possible explanation for the fantastic pledges the Chinese make to themselves. In any event, one can be sure that these deceptions have not really affected the hearts and minds of the Chinese people.

But examples of these distortions and eyewash are manifold. Thus, the Chinese doctors promised to eliminate cancer in three years; agricultural workers of a certain region promised to increase the harvest by 300 per cent in three years—and of course, there is still cancer in China and the harvests have not tripled. Or another example, concerning the utilization of ultrasonic equipment, which, in 1960, the Chinese Communist Party declared essential to the modernization of industry. Complex and delicate instruments were built at astronomical costs, but, in nearly every case, they could not be used because no thought had been put into what and how they would contribute to Chinese industrial growth.

In any event, one thing is certain: Mao is "omniscient," and his power allows him to carry out on the immense crowd of humanity over which he rules whatever idea comes to his mind. Opposition is unthinkable. The only means of defense against the stupidity or injuriousness of government orders are precisely these lies, eyewash, and announcements of fantastic achievement, for only the manifestation of the most perfect obedience permits one to survive. In China, as in other Communist countries, the eyewash is not only the result of bad faith among the leaders, not only the result of government control and propaganda: It is the ineluctable consequence of the relations, based on lies and falsification, that have been established between the administrators and the administered, between the superior cadres and the executors of their orders. This eyewash and deception has become the dominating characteristic of modern China, relegating to the background all the ideological campaigns and the famous "brainwashing."

One can compare the manner in which Mao governs China to

the way in which a drunken busdriver would conduct his crowded bus along a precipitous and curving mountain road. The number of passengers who realize the danger grows with each passing moment, but no one dares to push the driver out of the way and take over himself the responsibility of guiding the vehicle to safety. For, in truth, political power is like alcohol in its ability to intoxicate. The best driver in the world, if he is inebriated, is good for nothing; at a certain point, his blood becomes saturated and beyond that point, his training is of no further use.

The Austrian Hitler, the Georgian Stalin, the Chinese Mao—despite the great differences in their origin and training—displayed frightening resemblances in the way they conducted themselves as heads of state. A dictator pretends in vain to act in the name of certain classes—he belongs to none of them, he is a dictator and his own interests are contrary to those of the people he pretends to defend.

The psychology of the despot is deeply influenced by the very fact that his every wish is executed. We know what happens to a spoiled child: He becomes egoistical, authoritarian, and believes the world was made to satisfy his desires. The only difference between a spoiled child and a dictator is that the dictator affirms that his caprices are based on theories or ideologies, be they national-socialist or Communist. Thus does he camouflage his rapaciousness and hunger for power and glory.

Now China has unquestionably arrived at a very dangerous moment in her national history, but there are several roads she can take that will, in the end, lead her beyond her present difficulties. The question is only to determine what price she is willing to pay. No longer is there talk of the Great Leap Forward, but of the new formula of Step-by-Step Progression. Yet formulas are of little importance: As long as Mao Tse-tung is in power, China will stagnate. If Mao disappears, the situation in China would improve instantaneously. For one thing, even if the same officers who now surround him remained in power, it is certain they would behave more realistically. For another, the mere desire not to lose power would prevent them from destroying those qualities of the system that assure them all of benefits and continued power. Another factor that would operate to prevent the reconstitution of a single authority such as Mao now wields, is the formation in China, similar to that in Russia, of a new ruling class, intent upon preserving its privileges and maintaining its authority. The directors of plants and factories, the younger cadres, the survivors of older groups of cadres will certainly play a decisive role in the organization of their country.

Mao is not eternal. His power will crumble, and the Chinese, who have proved themselves in adversity throughout their long history, will triumph then as well. For it is an indisputable law of history: The people will survive, and the people will triumph.

How many monuments erected in honor of a tyrant, whose name has now fallen into oblivion, are today remembered with nothing but admiration for the unknown and unnamed who labored to construct them! For those who know of the labors and the suffering of the Chinese people, the comparison with ancient Egypt comes inevitably to mind. It will come to pass that the Chinese people—patient, hard-working, gifted in the sciences and the arts—will one day live in peace and prosperity, and will once again be free to make their inestimable contribution to universal culture and the progress of humanity.

DATE DUE